ARCHAEOLOGY OF THE CINEMA

293 illustrations

Archaeology of the CINEMA

C. W. CERAM

NEW YORK
HARCOURT, BRACE & WORLD, INC.

ILLUSTRATIONS EDITOR: OLIVE COOK

TRANSLATED BY RICHARD WINSTON

First American edition

Library of Congress Catalog Card Number: 65–19106

Printed in Germany by Mohn & Co. Gütersloh

CONTENTS

The illustration on the title page is from
Kircher's *Ars Magna Lucis et Umbrae* (1643)
demonstrating the principle of projection

The purpose of this book is to make order out of a vast amount of material which has been accumulating for decades: the prehistory and early history of the cinema. What I am really concerned with is the genesis of the cinema as a technique, and my book ends at 1897, the year which saw the birth of the cinema *industry*. I have tried to leave out inessentials, although they are sometimes highly interesting, and to present essentials, which are sometimes uninteresting. In line with this, I have tried to give at least thumbnail sketches of the careers of men who were responsible for the development of the cinema.

The facts have been sifted again and again. I did my first writing on the archaeology of the cinema as long ago as 1936. At that time I interviewed Max Skladanowsky and Oskar Messter in Berlin, and Louis Lumière in Paris. After the war I was able to examine the archives of the *Deutsches Institut für Filmkunde* in Biebrich Castle, and with the assistance of my friend Heinrich Fraenkel (author of *Unsterblicher Film*, Munich, 1956) was able to work in the British Film Institute in London. I also had the privilege of assistance from Lotte Eisner in the Cinématèque Française in Paris (where I saw all the Méliès films) and rounded out my study in the magnificent film library of New York's Museum of Modern Art and, with the kind aid of Herbert and Josine Kline, at the Lytton Center of the Visual Arts in Hollywood.

Particular thanks are due to Olive Cook for her help. She has made some extremely valuable suggestions and in collaboration with the publishers, Thames and Hudson, also collected the illustrations, which in several cases were extremely difficult to come by.

These illustrations are far more than an addition to the book. They are an essential extension to the text, and also include cultural forerunners of the cinema which although not described in the text are included here to round off the technical history of the subject.

Edison, Thomas Alva, 1847–1931, famous American inventor ... In 1887 he perfected the Kinetoscope into the moving picture machine.

THE NEW AMERICAN ENCYCLOPEDIA,
REVISED EDITION. NEW YORK, 1942

Here lies William Friese Greene, born 7th Sept. 1855, died 5th May 1921, also his wife Edith Jane, born 1856, died 20th July 1921. The inventor of Kinematography. His genius bestowed upon humanity the boon of commercial kinematography of which he was the first inventor and patentee. (June 21st, 1889, N⁰ 10,301)

INSCRIPTION ON GRAVESTONE IN
HIGHGATE CEMETERY, LONDON

Ici le 28 décembre 1895 eurent lieu les premières projections publiques de photographie animée à l'aide du cinématographe appareil inventé par les frères Lumières.

MEMORIAL PLAQUE ON THE BUILDING IN PARIS
IN WHICH THE GRAND CAFÉ WAS FORMERLY LOCATED

In diesem Hause fanden am 1. November 1895 die ersten öffentlichen Filmvorführungen in Europa durch Max und Emil Skladanowsky statt mit Hilfe eigens aufgenommener Filme und selbst erfundener Apparate des Max Skladanowsky.

MEMORIAL PLAQUE AT THE WINTERGARTEN,
THE BERLIN VARIETY THEATRE

Jeune homme, remerciez-moi. Mon invention n'est pas à vendre, mais pour vous, elle serait la ruine. Elle peut être exploitée quelque temps comme une curiosité scientifique: en dehors de cela elle n'a aucun avenir commercial.

LOUIS LUMIÈRE, 1895

Le cinéma? Je n'y vais plus. Si j'avais pu prevoir qu'on en viendrait là, je ne l'aurais pas inventé.

LOUIS LUMIÈRE, ABOUT 1930

Dubious and serious forerunners

According to one fine, pithy definition, a 'film' is a 'photographic projection of continuous images'.[1] According to another it is 'in contrast to chronophotography, a technical device for achieving the illusion of motion by photographic means'.[2] Both these definitions, of course, only describe a technical procedure. The 1932 edition of the *Brockhaus* encyclopedia distinguishes sharply between film as a celluloid strip and 'cinematography'. If I ask for film in a camera shop, I will obtain a light-sensitive roll of celluloid. If I pay admission to the cinema, I will see a documentary or a feature film – in the old days a silent film, nowadays a sound film, frequently not a celluloid but a plastic film in the numerous wide-screen processes from Cinemascope to Cinerama. The Englishman goes 'to the cinema', the America 'to the movies', the South African even nowadays says he is going to the bioscope. Only the pretentious go to the motion pictures (though the word is still used to demark the cinema from other representational arts). People who affect outmoded slang will sometimes speak of going 'to the flicks'. The celluloid strip is film, but we may also say: 'I am going to see that film'. We may speak of 'The History of the Film', but more precisely of 'The Invention of the Cinema'. The Frenchman has enlarged the meaning of the word 'cinéma';

he goes to the 'cinéma', but also speaks of the 'Histoire du Cinéma'. 'Le film' is a particular work; there are also 'les films allemands'. For the celluloid strip proper he has the word 'la pellicule'.

A German Doctor of Philosophy has handed down a definition whose comprehensiveness is a little staggering: 'The film is the chemico-technical fixation process of a movement for the purpose of achieving a motion-filled pictorial reproduction of an event by means of an apparatus which has been developed on the basis of knowledge of physiological and psychological facts. Its pictorial representation can be meaningfully influenced in correspondence with its intellectual content, en route from photography to projection, by knowledgeable manipulation of technical and chemical methods. The ultimate purpose of the film is the presentation of an assemblage of individual units which are to be influenced by the motion-filled reproduction of a rationally ordered succession of actions.'[3]

Passing beyond definitions, there are the economist's statement: 'The fifth largest industry in the world'; the journalist's metaphors: 'Dream factory' and 'Fantasy machine'[4]; the judgement of an enthusiastic critic: 'The art of the twentieth century'. (In 1921 a French cinema club called itself the 'Club des Amis du VIIe Art').

We hope that this history of the cinema will also throw some light upon the deeper meaning of the medium.

Cinema begins with cinematography, a term which refers to the 'technical apparatus' of the cinema. It is a mistake to ask when the cinema was invented. Only cinematography was invented. The cinema is far more than an apparatus, and it was not invented; it 'growed'.

Cinematography as an assemblage of technical apparatus is the sum of inventions and discoveries which were made chiefly in the nineteenth century. That was the century in which 'technology' in general was developed, and then only in the West. Classical antiquity was familiar with mathematics, physics, and chemistry in the form of alchemy. Translated into practical terms, these sciences yielded mechanics, but not technology. Mechanics are static while technology is dynamic, is 'putting nature to the question by torture'[5] – is, in a word, the subjugation of *energy*.

Thus cinematography, the product of sciences become dynamic, began in the nineteenth century; the suggestions advanced by Heron of Alexandria[6] remained dormant, for the spirit of his age was static. So, too, nothing came of the insights of Claudius Ptolemy[7] or of Ibn al Haitam.[8] All the speculation about a few obscure lines on 'moving pictures' in Lucretius[9] is absurd. Even more ridiculous is the attempt to connect the cave paintings of Altamira, the Egyptian series reliefs, the friezes on mausoleums and the Parthenon, with the nineteenth century's 'living series pictures'.[10] All such efforts stem from a fondness for mechanistic theories of evolution, from a tendency to see the history of civilised man as a continuously progressive process going on for five thousand years. In fact there is no more connection between the early concepts of images in series and the cinema than there is between the landings of the Vikings in Vinland with Columbus' discovery of Central America in 1492. What matters in history is not whether certain chance discoveries take place, but whether they take effect. And in this sense the only discoveries which took effect and became indispensable parts of the sum which ultimately would be called cinematography were those made between 1792 and 1888. The engineer Rudolph Thun[11] has classified these discoveries in terms of their underlying technical principles. This is how he charts it:

Reproduction of motion by changing 'phase pictures'.
Reproduction of constantly moving pictures by rapidly moving slots.
Intermittent motion of the phase pictures with approximate or complete periods of rest.
Optical compensation for the motion of the phase pictures by lens and mirror.
Long strips of pictures.
Projection of moving pictures.

These final stages could not have been achieved without knowledge of the 'stroboscopic effect', that is, the persistence of vision. This knowledge had existed in pragmatic form for centuries, but no use had been made of it. Further requirements were some sort of method for projecting images with the aid of lenses (magic lantern, known since 1646), and the invention of photography (the first daguerreotypes appeared in 1839).

Let us without more ado rule out an additional angle: Knowledge of automatons, or of clockwork toys, played no part in the story of cinematography, nor is there any link between it and the production of animated 'scenes'. We can therefore omit from our discussion the Chinese, Indian and Javanese shadow-plays, the baroque automatons, and the marionette theatre. Even the 'deviltries' of Porta,[12] produced with the camera obscura, the phantasmagorias of Robertson,[13] the 'dissolving views' of Child,[14] are not to the point. All these discoveries did not lead to the first genuine moving picture sequence. From the nature of the mechanisms involved and the trifling uses to which they were put, they belonged to the upper classes,[15] to small groups (except for the shadow-plays of the Orient, which were in fact popular entertainment, but had nothing to do with technology and were solely matters of manual skill). They essentially belong to the cultural history of the late Middle Ages and pre-technological period of the nineteenth century. The Phantasmagorias have no more to do with the Lumière brothers' cinematograph theatre than the automaton called 'the writer' fabricated by Jacques Dros has to do with a modern printing press, or Baron Karl Drais von Sauerbronn's velocipede with a motorcycle. In all these cases, there is no question of 'evolution' from the one to the other. Between these inventions a mutation intervened, the change from mechanical to technical thinking.[16]

Incidentally, the thaumatrope[17] and the slides[18] of the magic lantern do not qualify as cinematography for purely technical

reasons. The first did not show movement; it merely transformed two different states of a picture into a new state by an
illusion of identification. The slides, too, did not show genuine
motion, but merely 'change of position'.

It would have been altogether unnecessary even to mention
these experiments and devices, were it not for the fact that
previous writers on the subject have inevitably included them
in their annals.[19]

The prehistory of cinematography begins at a perfectly specific time, the year 1832, 'with Plateau's Phenakisticope and
Stampfer's Stroboscope'.

Joseph Antoine Ferdinand Plateau (1801–1883) published his
first investigations of the 'persistence of vision' in 1829. In 1836
he established the laws of the 'stroboscopic effect'. To put it
briefly, he had rediscovered the following fact: If sixteen pictures are made of a movement, which takes place in a second,
and if these sixteen pictures are shown successively to the eye
in one second, the laggard sense of sight puts them together and
sees them as the original movement.

In 1832 Plateau constructed a device giving the illusion of
movement. Concurrently and independently of him, Simon
Ritter von Stampfer, Professor of Geometry at the Vienna
Polytechnical Institute, made the same invention. Plateau
called his a Phenakisticope; Stampfer gave his device the name
of Stroboscope. The device consisted of a slotted disc[20] round
which twelve or more phase drawings were arranged in order.

When this disc was rotated in front of a mirror, the reflected image viewed through the slots was seen in continuous motion. It is important to point out that in this and most of the similar devices which followed it, the effect of motion was caused by an arrangement of phase pictures in which the last phase passed into the first. In other words, there was an endless series, an everlastingly repeated motion. A runner, for example, ran on the spot, without moving forward.[21]

The same principle, though slightly modified, underlay the wheel of life, called both Zootrope and Zoètrope (originally Daedelum), invented by William George Horner (1786–1837) in 1834. A band of pictures was mounted inside a revolving drum, and viewed through slots in the outside of the drum. The band was detachable and could be changed at will. In 1877 Emile Reynaud (1844–1918) developed the Praxinoscope, a significant improvement on the Zootrope because an arrangement of mirrors inside a polygonal drum produced an 'optical compensation' which did away with the phases of darkness between individual pictures.

The first drawn pictures had come to 'life'. Shortly afterwards, the living drawings were projected for the first time.

In 1646 the Jesuit Father Athanasius Kircher[22] had outlined the principles of the magic lantern in his book, *Ars magna lucis et umbrae*. An Austrian artillery officer, Baron Franz von Uchatius, combined the possibility of projection offered by the magic lantern with the principle of the Phenakisticope in a remarkable fashion. He arranged a number of magic lanterns in a semicircle so that they were focused on a wall screen, filled them with drawn diapositives (phase pictures), and moved a torch very rapidly around the semicircle behind them. He discovered that as the pictures flashed on the screen one after another, motion resulted. In 1853 he constructed a new projection apparatus which could show twelve phases, with the diapositives arranged in a circle. Whereas the Phenakisticope could be seen by only one person at a time, the Uchatius apparatus could show its projected images to a whole room of spectators. This was a significant technical advance.[23]

Uchatius (1811–1881), incidentally, is a figure who deserves a new biography. He was not only a military man, but also a trained chemist and photographer, physicist, and maker of cannon (an eternally unfortunate Austrian rival of Krupp in the construction of steel cannon barrels). As far as he was concerned, his dabbling in cinematography was a mere hobby. Light-heartedly, he sold his apparatus to a Viennese prestidigitator named Ludwig Döbler (1801–1864), who made such a good thing of it that he was able to spend his declining years in a castle. Uchatius, despite his rapid advance in the army, won no recognition for his scientific work; a deeply unhappy man, he ultimately committed suicide.[24]

The pictures for these instruments, however, were still being drawn. The next steps on the road to cinematography were taken not by skilled mechanicians, but by chemists. Shortly after Horner's Zoetrope was invented, an Englishman was already engaged in the first attempts at photography.

1 See Traub: *Als man anfing zu filmen* (Berlin, 1940).
2 See Reinert: *Kleines Filmlexikon* (Zurich, 1946), p. 113.
3 Walter Panofsky: *Die Geburt des Films* (Würzburg, 1944), p. 3.
4 Titles of books by Ilya Ehrenburg and René Fülöp-Miller.
5 Oswald Spengler: *Der Mensch und die Technik*, p. 67 ff., and Merckel: *Ingenieurtechnik im Altertum*.
6 *c.* AD 125. Description of 'mirror writing' and 'phantom mirrors' in *Peri automatopoietikes* (Construction of automaton theatres).
7 *c.* AD 150. First description of the after-image effect in the *Optica* (preserved only in Latin translation from the Arabic).
8 Known as Alhazen, died 1038; first description of the principle of the camera obscura.
9 Titus Lucretius Carus (*c.* 98–55 BC) in *De rerum natura*, IV, 768 ff. The verses probably describe the generation of dream-images. But the uniqueness of the description is scarcely proof that Lucretius had not witnessed a projection of shadow-pictures. Elevators, for example, are never mentioned in ancient literature; nevertheless they existed (Lamer: *Wörterbuch der Antike*).

10 Particularly stressed in J. Gregor: *Das Zeitalter des Films* (Vienna, 1932), but also by many other writers.

11 Rudolph Thun: *Entwicklung der Kinotechnik* (Berlin, 1936).

12 Giovanni Battista della Porta (1540–1615) in *Magia naturalis* (Naples, 1553) describes again (after Alhazen and Leonardo da Vinci) the camera obscura. The later 'deviltries' were conjured up for a public *inside* the camera obscura by a performer dancing in front of a hole in the 'dark chamber'. The camera obscura was a forerunner of the photographic camera, but not of the cinema projector.

13 Etienne Gaspard Robert (called Robertson) (1763–1837), from about 1795 on, using a movable magic lantern directed at a double or triple layer of gauze curtain, produced eerie pictures of ghosts, gods, and kings. The curtain hung *between* the public and the magic lantern; the impression of movement was evoked by changes in the size of the pictures resulting from the magic lantern's being moved back and forth. Robertson, incidentally, was for a time the victim of political censorship. In post-revolutionary Paris he made the ghosts of dead heroes of the Revolution appear on his gauze, or on smoke. When he ventured to conjure the ghost of Louis XVI, the authorities closed down his theatre.

14 In 1840 H. L. Child, by alternately brightening and dimming lights from several sources placed behind a number of sliding painted glass plates, produced moving projections,

so-called 'dissolving views'. This was a spurious kind of motion picture, for although he could show a wagon passing over a landscape, the wheels did not turn. The idea had been anticipated by Pieter van Musschenbroek (1692 to 1761), a Dutch mathematician, who proposed the use of several glass plates, painted and capable of being slid past one another, to show ships on an active sea, windmills turning, persons greeting one another. It is probable that he actually experimented with such effects.

15 Yet the elaborate optical entertainments of the late eighteenth and nineteenth centuries, the Eidophusikon, the Panorama, Diorama and associated spectacles commanded huge audiences. In London alone there were as many Diorama and Panorama buildings as there are cinemas today.

16 Fr. G. Jünger: *Die Perfektion der Technik*, p. 145 f.

17 Invented by Dr J. A. Paris (1785–1856). For example, a disk with a parrot painted on one side and a cage on the other; when rotated swiftly, the bird appeared inside the cage.

18 Two transparent glass plates with two different phases of motion produce the illusion of a change of position when moved past one another.

19 Discussed at particular length by Sadoul in volume I of his otherwise excellent *Histoire générale du cinéma* (Paris, 1948 ff.). Zglinicki in *Der Weg des Films* (Berlin, 1956) has covered the subject with prodigious industry.

20 Originally only a disk which had to be viewed in front of a mirror.

21 Traub in *Als man anfing zu filmen* rightly sees in the distinction between these endless, circular 'picture sequences' *(Reihenbilder)* and the later 'continuous pictures' *(Laufbilder)* (with altogether different movements at the end of the strip from those shown at the beginning) one of the few elements whereby we may introduce a certain order in the technical prehistory of the cinema, and evaluate discoveries.

22 Athanasius Kircher (1601–1680), learned in mathematics and Hebrew, studied Egyptian hieroglyphs. *Autobiography* (1685); German translation by N. Seng (1901). Magic lantern: A camera obscura with its function 'reversed and activated' by the use of lenses. All projection devices are based on the idea of the magic lantern.

23 Drawn pictures were furthermore projected in 1866 by means of Beale's Chorentoscope, an instrument which was similar in principle to the modern Maltese Cross projector with a front shutter to mask each successive phase of motion.

24 Rudolf Thiel: *Ruhm und Leiden der Erfinder* (Berlin, 1942); Kurzel-Runtscheiner: *Franz Freiherr von Uchatius*. Blätter für Geschichte der Technik, Heft 4 (Vienna, 1938).

Cinematography is technically based on the phenomenon o persistence of vision – the capacity of the retina of the eye t retain the impression of an object for the fraction of a secon after its disappearance. The Phenakisticope (opposite) of 183 was the first device based on this phenomenon to reconstitu movement from a number of individual pictures of successiv phases of motion. This invention was the progenitor of all th later and more complicated forms of motion picture. (1)

Shadow entertainments have no di
technical connection with the cinema,
the affinity is obvious. In their consistent
of the animated two-dimensional image fl
upon a screen and their wide range of sub
matter they are more akin to the motion p
ture than any of its cultural forerunners.
The shadow show originated in the Far E
Simple devices for projecting shadows in
ded the Chinese perforated metal ball
the Japanese magic mirror. The filigree p
terns on the ball are thrown upon the w
by means of a lighted candle inside it wh
remains upright when the ball is rolled. W
a strong light is reflected from the polish
slightly convex face of the mirror the im
on the back appears as a shadow on the w
(2, 3)

…ese **shadow plays**, sometimes, like early films, …n in serial form, embrace religious, legendary, …ric, satirical and domestic themes. The stylised …ets, jointed at the shoulders, elbows and hips …nade of sheepskin or skin from the donkey's … and painted in translucent colours that glow …gh the screen. Different heads can be fitted to …ame figure by means of a slot in the collar. (4)

Javanese puppets are even more conventionalised and are manipulated by means of rods attached to their immensely long, articulated arms. They are painted and gilded but made of thick buffalo hide which casts a black shadow. The exotic stories they enact, taken from the great national epics, have much in common with the chaotic, mythological films made earlier in this century by the Shadra Film Company, Bombay. (5)

The Turkish shadow show takes its name from Karagöz, its principle figure, a slapstick comic character, one of the most notable ancestors of the clowns of the celluloid. The shadows cast by two Karagöz puppets are shown on the right. Of painted translucent camel skin which throws coloured shadows, they have typically minute feet and short arms. (6)

göz dominated the shadow enter-
ment of Egypt, North Africa and
ce and inevitably influenced sha-
play in Europe. Left, a 19th cen-
lithograph of a shadow show in
ers; and above, a scene from the
ow play *Kazandonis*, a modern
tation of Karagöz performed in
ns. (7, 8)

English moving shadow lantern
(right), metal cut and articulat-
s in much the same farcical tra-
n as the Karagöz shadows. The
e by which the shadow show be-
 generally known in Europe, *Om-
Chinoises*, is misleading, for it was
kish influence together with the
 for the silhouette which fostered
hadow play in the West. (9)

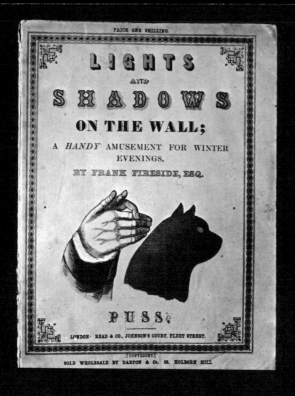

The popularity of the Ombres Chinoises in Europe during the 19th century was reflected in the publication of numerous juvenile shadow shows and manuals on hand shadows which were also the subject of instructive lantern slides (above). Street shows were given by wandering showmen from the early 18th century onwards and among the earlier permanent shadow theatres was that of F. D. Séraphin in the Palais Royale, opened in 1784. A group of Séraphin's puppets is shown above right. (10–13)

Le Ballet de Cendrillon

e metal cut huntsman (below), worked by wheels, levers and
leys below stage, was shown in the entirely mechanical Char-
anier-Cottier shadow theatre at Geneva. The silhouette by
uis Morin was used in Salis's famous Théâtre des Ombres du
at Noir, opened in 1881. It is cut out of zinc and not articulat-
The perforated shadow card illustrates a device employed at
Chat Noir to form an image with all the appropriate lights
d shades of a black and white drawing. (14–16)

Famous shadow showmen of the late
century included F. Trewey of the Em
Theatre and G. Méliès, director of the T
tre Robert Houdin. Méliès, silhouettes
L'Auberge du Diable appear on the left. I
men were later connected with the cine
Trewey became Lumière's projectionist
London manager while Méliès was the n
spectacular of the pioneer film makers.
fantastic fairy-tale themes continued the
dition of the shadow show. (17, 18)

...ondensing lens, an important feature
...evolution of projection, was anticipated
...onardo (right) in this drawing of a
...eye lantern made nearly two centuries
... the actual appearance of the magic
...n. (19)

...ptical or magic lantern, the forerunner
... cinema projector, was known in the
...century, when it is said to have been
...ted by Father Athanasius Kircher, a
... priest who outlined the principles of
...ction in his book *Ars Magna Lucis et
...ae* (1646). Two illustrations from this
... a demonstration of the properties of
...ns and the projection of a slide, appear
... with a portrait of Kircher engraved in
... (20–22)

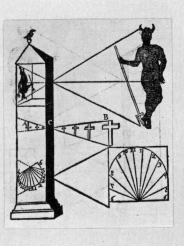

The combination of projector and motion pictures was achieved in principle before the close of the 17th century by Johannes Zahn, author of *Occulis Artificialis* (1685 and 1702), and one of several inventors who contributed to the perfection of Kircher's optical lantern. Zahn showed glass slides mounted on a circular disc (above right) which could be revolved in front of the magic lantern lens to give an impression of movement. This method of projecting a series of images was used with scarcely any modification by 19th century experimenters (see Nos 90, 158). The table model projector invented by Zahn set the pattern for the magic lantern to the end of the 19th century. The two late 18th century lanterns shown here, and the engraving of a lantern from Hooper's *Rational Recreations* (1774) all derive from Zahn's model. (24–27)

The engraving above shows one of the curious purposes to which Zahn adapted the lantern: it has become an automatic wind indicator, the projected wind instrument being connected with a vane on the roof. (23)

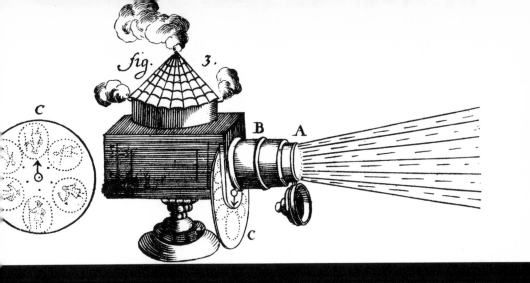

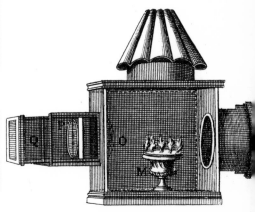

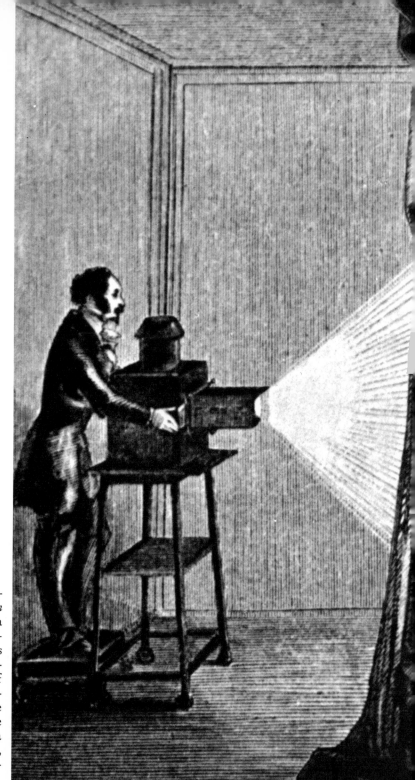

The Phantasmagoria, engraving from *Le Magasin Pittoresque*, 1845, was a magic lantern entertainment popularized in Paris by E. G. Robertson, a Belgian, towards the close of the 18th century. The lantern is hidden from the audience so that the image, projected onto a thin, transparent screen, has the force of an apparition. (28)

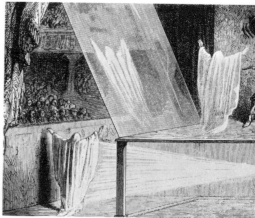

The effect of Robertson's entertainment was enhanced by its setting in the abandoned chapel of a Capuchin monastery near the Place Vendôme. Two contemporary impressions of the show are reproduced here, dating from 1797 (below far left) and 1798 (above). The apparitions and spectres were made to advance or withdraw by means of lenses and concave reflectors, creating effects which have their counterparts in the modern cinema theatre. The extent to which this macabre entertainment captivated the taste of the times is reflected in Gillray's choice of subject for his caricature of the Peace of Amiens (left). (29–31)

An effect similar to those exhibited by the Phantasmagoria is shown below: a ghost is conjured up in the theatre with the aid of a lantern and huge sheets of glass. (32)

These trick displays contrast with the equally popular straightforward magic lantern show (below) in which, as in the cinema, the projector is on the same side of the screen as the spectator. Below, left, French engraving, 1810. Right, *The Magic Lantern* published by J. Johnston, Nov. 1st 1822. An interesting feature of this drawing-room entertainment is the provision of a musical accompaniment. (33, 34)

THE MAGIC LANTERN

merant magic lantern showman such as were common in the
eets of all the larger European cities during the early years of
e last century, from a lithograph by Gavarni. The lantern he
rries closely resembles that on the extreme left of the middle
lf in this showcase of simple 18th and 19th century lanterns
d slides from the Barnes Museum of Cinematography. (35, 36)

The introduction of the Lampascope testifies to the widespread taste for the magic lantern entertainment in the home during the middle years of the 19th century. The ordinary paraffin table lamp was used as the illuminant, the Lampascope taking the place of the glass globe of the lamp. The slide in position in the Lampascope is the simplest form of glass to create a sense of movement. It contains a series of images which are passed slowly in front of the lens. The characteristic subjects of the three hand painted 'panoramic' slides shown below are *Noah's Ark, The Retreat from Moscow* and *The Mad Bull*. (37, 38)

Among the many types of slides shown in Victorian lantern displays, the extremely skilfully painted panoramic glass of Paris and the scene from a series based on *Uncle Tom's Cabin* (right), illustrate two characteristic forms of lantern entertainment of the period, the instructive and the narrative. (39, 40)

The desire to animate the projected image led to the invention of mechanical slides. The lever slide, of which two examples are shown above, combines two glasses, one of which is worked up and down over the other. The rackwork slide achieves motion through the action of rack and pinion, one of its two glasses being set in a cogged frame. This example (below left) is one of a series of hand painted instructive slides made by Carpenter and Westley to demonstrate the diurnal motion of the earth and the courses

the planets. Pulley slides (centre) consist of two glass discs
mounted in brass rings and turned in contrary directions by
means of two bands. This kind of frame was used for the very
popular Chromatropes showing rapidly expanding and contract-
ing patterns of brilliant colour. The discs are painted alike with
concentric ray or linear designs. The Chromatrope derived from
the Eidotrope (right) which consisted of two pierced discs revolving in opposite directions to project moving shadows patterns. (41–45)

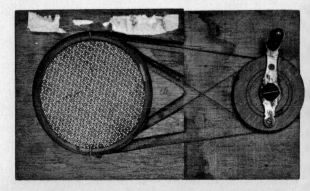

In the sophisticated lantern displays of the late 19th century m
ment was created by means of elaborate lighting effects and by th
of dissolvers and multiple lenses. Foremost among the many impr
oil lanterns was the Sciopticon (top left) an American invention
vided with four flat wicks and heat-resisting conoidal glasses. Th
lamp was succeeded by limelight, a powerful illuminant produce
impinging a flame resulting from the combustion of oxygen and hy
gen gas against a cylinder of hard lime. The lantern below the S
ticon is fitted with a blow-through limelight jet and also a fan diss
(one of a pair) by means of which one picture was made to fade g
ually away as another took its place. A similar effect was also achi
by biunial (right) and triple (below left) lanterns where the lenses
so adjusted that the projected images perfectly coincided, allowing
picture to merge into another with a distinct sense of movement. (4

The compressed or distorted image of the modern cinemascope
is restored by means of the anamorphic lens. This principle had
demonstrated as early as the 16th century and was incorporated
popular 19th century toy, a polished metal cylinder which refl
coherent images from distorted drawings known as anamorphic
tures. (50, 51)

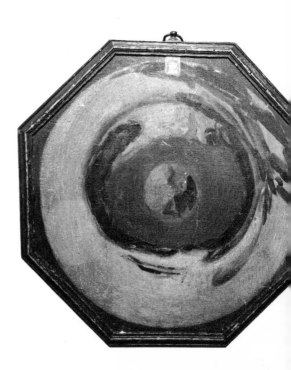

Anamorphic portrait of Edward VI, 1546[?] distorted image is in this case corrected[?] looking at the picture from a side angle. (5 2[?]

Perspective tricks, mirrors and special le[?] are among the means employed to create an[?] sion of three-dimensional reality on a[?] dimensional film screen. These were also[?] methods to which the makers of peepshow[?] sorted. The interior opposite is seen throug[?] eyepiece fitted with a lens in a so-called[?] spective box' made by Samuel van Hoogstra[?] c. 1650. The rectangular box is painted onl[?] the sides and bottom. The illusion of t[?] dimensional reality is produced by a comb[?] tion of skilful perspective, the enhancing p[?] of the lens, and light reflected from inc[?] mirrors. (54)

Peepshows were among the commonest entertainments of the street and fairground throughout the 18th and 19th centuries. The example on the right (from an engraving dated 1798) has eyepieces for three viewers. The showman would let down successive scenes by means of the strings at the side, usually sensational episodes from contemporary life, accompanying the display with a lively commentary. The scenes were probably lit from behind by a row of tallow candles. (55)

peepshows took the form of a
f panels set up one behind the
o form a perspective view seen
h a lens and lit from behind. The
19th century peepshow above,
rom the side, shows the Place
me. The peepshow at South-
air (left) engraved by Hogarth
ave resembled this French peep-
or it may have been a perspec-
x. (56, 57)
ure alabaster peepshows, known
p-eggs, were sold as souvenirs
hout the Victorian period. Each
ntained two alternating scenes,
through a double convex, won-
y transforming lens. (58)

The Kaleidoscope, like the perspective box, employs a lens and reflectors. It was invented by Sir David Brewster (above) in 1816; his *Treatise on the Kaleidoscope* was published in 1819. The instrument exhibits an infinite variety of changing symmetrical patterns by means of successive reflectors. In its simplest form it consists of two reflectors placed together at a particular angle with an object box at one end containing pieces of coloured glass. Right, German kaleidoscope on a wooden stand, *c.* 1860, a simple kaleidoscope, a Victorian polygonal kaleidoscope with three reflectors and, in the foreground, a kaleidoscope for viewing opaque objects, *c.* 1830. (59, 60)

PROSPECTUS OF AN EXHIBITION

TO BE CALLED THE

Eidophusikon.

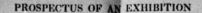

W. DALBERG,

A German Artist, in reviving this Exhibition, (originally produced by the celebrated De Loutherbourg,) begs leave to present to the Nobility and Gentry, a description of his intended Exhibition. The Interior will be a Model of a beautiful Classic Theatre ; the dimensions of the stage, 10 feet by 12; devoted entirely for Picturesque Scenery, Panoramas, Dioramas, and Physioramas. The following is a Programme of the Scenery :

SCENE 1.

A view from the summit of One Tree Hill, in Greenwich Park, looking up the Thames to the Metropolis ; on one side, conspicuous upon its picturesque eminence, will stand Flamstead House ; and below, on the right, that grand mass of building, GREENWICH HOSPITAL, with its imposing Cupola, cut out of pasteboard, and painted with architectural exactness. The large group of Trees forming another division, beyond which the Towns of Greenwich and Deptford, with the shore on each side stretching to the Metropolis. In the distance will be seen the hills of Hampstead, Highgate, and Harrow ; and the intermediate space will be occupied as the pool, or port of London, crowded with Shipping, each mass of which will be cut out of pasteboard, and receding in size by the perspective of their distance. On the rising of the Curtain, the scene will be enveloped in that mysterious light which is the precursor of day-break ; the mist will clear away, the picture brighten by degrees, until it assumes the appearance of a beauteous summer's day, gilding the tops of the trees and the projections of the lofty buildings; the clouds will pass to a clear and beautiful moon-light night. To make the view as true to Nature as art will allow, the Shipping and Steam Boats will sail up and down the River.

SCENE 2.

Diorama of the "Ladyes Chapel," Southwark, with the effects of Light and Shade.

SCENE 3.

The effect of a Storm at Sea, in which will be described all the characteristic horrors of wind, hail, thunder, lightning, and the roaring of the waves, with the loss of an East Indiaman.

SCENE 4.

A moving Panorama of English Scenery, from Windsor to Eton, the Exhibition of which was so universally admired at Drury Lane Theatre.

SCENE 5.

A Calm, with an Italian Sea Port, in which will be represented the rising of the Moon, the Mountains, and the Water will be finally contrasted by a lofty Light House of picturesque

The counterparts of the humble peepshow in the fashionable world were elaborate optical spectacles, the most widely patronized of which were the Panorama and Diorama, the essential character of which is conveyed on a tiny scale by the toy strip panorama above. These entertainments were preceded by the Eidophusikon invented by Philip Jacob de Loutherbourg in 1781. This was basically a peepshow which, like the cinema, would hold the spectators as well as the moving image. (61, 62)

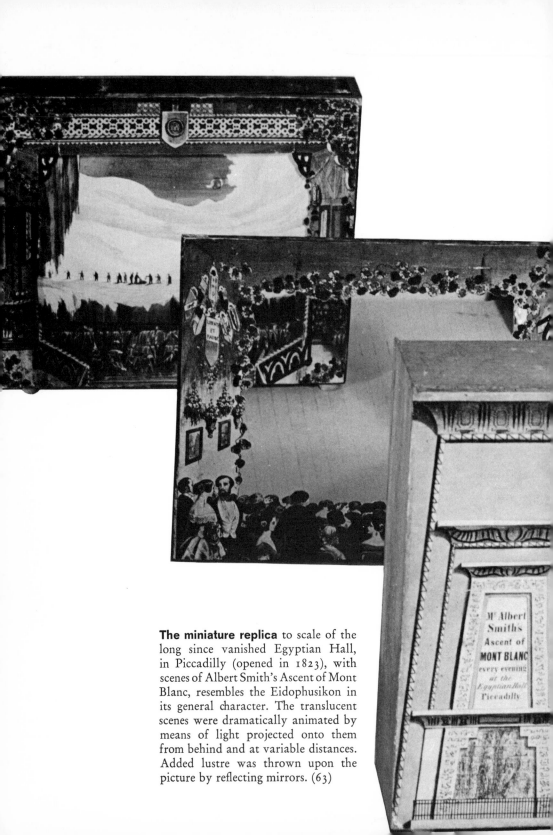

The miniature replica to scale of the long since vanished Egyptian Hall, in Piccadilly (opened in 1823), with scenes of Albert Smith's Ascent of Mont Blanc, resembles the Eidophusikon in its general character. The translucent scenes were dramatically animated by means of light projected onto them from behind and at variable distances. Added lustre was thrown upon the picture by reflecting mirrors. (63)

The invention of the Panorama is usually attributed to the painter Robert Barker who first exhibited the fully developed entertainment in Leicester Square in 1792. An enormous canvas attached to the inside of a rotunda revolved slowly round the spectators seated in the centre. The machinery of a panorama much resembled that of a post mill. Placed in semi-darkness in the middle of a circular platform, the audience gazed across a gulf of about 12 ft. at a continuous, moving picture lit from above. Barker's invention was taken to Paris and sold to a Mr and Mrs James Thayer who built two rotundas on the Boulevard Montmartre (above) in 1800. Panoramas soon began to multiply in all the chief cities of Europe and America. The subjects shown were mostly battle scenes or spectacular panoramic views, which the audience were enabled to follow by means of printed plans, sold as programmes, showing the auditorium and the encircling picture, with descriptive notes of the principle features or incidents. (64)

The Diorama, a brilliantly successful
entertainment, was invented by Daguer
first exhibited in a building he design
the purpose in the Rue Sanson, Paris (
in 1822. The Diorama consisted of g
transparent paintings exhibited under
ing light while the auditorium, whic
fitted with a single opening like a prosc
slowly revolved to move the spectator
one part of the picture to another.
background of the engraving can be se
cupola of a famous Panorama buildin
voted entirely to battle scenes devis
Colonel Langlois, and shown conti
from 1830 to 1870. The two posters
right (dated 1846 and 1831) testify to
spread interest in the Diorama. The Dio
of both M. R. Harrison at St Louis, Q
and of Martin at Birmingham were
style of Daguerre. (65–68)

RAND EXHIBITION
OF
LUMINATED DIORAMAS.

MR. M. R. HARRISON, ARTIST,
Begs most respectfully to inform the Ladies and Gentlemen of QUEBEC,
and its vicinity, that he will Exhibit his

LUMINATED CHEMICAL DIORAMAS,
(IN THE STYLE OF DAGUERRE,)

MONDAY EVENING, JUNE 8, 1846,
AND CONTINUE DURING THE WEEK,
AT THE

heatre Royal, St. Lewis.

H., as a Canadian Artist, confidently anticipates the patronage of those who would
nd encourage the Fine Arts. He has for many months devoted his whole time, and
ense outlay, to the study and perfecting of this beautiful style of painting.
ch Painting covers a surface of canvass nearly 200 square feet, representing two dis-
ctures, which, from the peculiar style of execution, and the varied nature and combina-
he illuminating-powers employed, produce changes the most astonishing, and at the
ne the most natural, in the power of the Artist to effect.

VIEW OF ORLEANS CATHEDRAL.

is Picture represents the grand front of Orleans Cathedral, which was founded by
n, in the sixty-ninth year of the Christian Era, and was enlarged by St. Eubert, and
essors. It was afterwards partly destroyed by the Northmen, and was re-constructed
l time by Robert De Corsie and Gillas Pastay, his successor, in 1287, and in the year
was again partly destroyed by the Calvinists, by springing of mines in the principal

e present Cathedral was constructed by Henry IVth, King of France, and Pope
the VIIIth. The interior is decorated with divers statues of great beauty, by the
ed Dugollan and Bourdin. This Cathedral is built in Gothic or pointed style, and is
red one of the best specimens on the Continent of Europe.
is Picture after passing through all the gradations of light, from day to night, will appear
gh illuminated by the silver beams of the rising moon; producing a surprising change
sky. The several windows of the surrounding buildings will be lit, and discover nume-
ures passing to and entering the Cathedral, which *will appear as when lit up for the*
on of Midnight Mass, displaying the Gothic painted windows, and part of the interior.

w of the City of Jerusalem and the Crucifixion.

is Picture, taken from the celebrated Painting by Martin, represents a distant view of
famed city. On the left will be perceived the crosses erected on Mount Cal-
the centre, the gates of entrance through the walls to the city, which, together with
nt and the adjacent country, will appear buried in repose, no figure at this time being
a gradual change will take place over the whole face of the picture, displaying the
s tints of the eastern sunset, until the sky assumes an awful and terrific aspect, oc-
illuminated by vivid flashes of lightning. The heavens will now appear to burst with
ight, gradually displaying the figures on the crosses, and the various groups compos-
subject of the Crucifixion. After a while, all will appear to recede and die away,
lace to the beautiful, calm and quiet appearance of the break of day.

THE CITY OF RAMESES,
AND THE
PARTURE OF THE ISRAELITES!

picture represents the City of Rameses, the Rendezvous of the children of Israel, from whence they took
rture from the land of Egypt.
y, or as some translate it, a fortress for the Egyptians. Its position may be fixed about six or eight miles
modern Cairo, a little to the north of the ancient Babylon of the Persians. The ancient Letopolis, as Jo-
ays, that the children of Israel after quitting this place in their march to Succoth, passed by the latter city
re is a copy from a celebrated painting by Roberts, and is considered one of the most beautiful specimens of
ral design. In the foreground to the left is the magnificent Palace of Pharaoh, which combined with the
 an heathen Gods, the Pyramids, &c., composes a picture of inconceivable beauty. During the first part of the
tion, not a figure will be seen, gradually the changes from noon to night come on when Pharaoh and his
scovered assembled in front of the royal palace, to witness the departure of the Israelites, with their camels,
&c., swelling into a countless multitude. The figure of Moses will be seen to occupy a position on the right
ral command.

ERIOR OF RHEIMS CATHEDRAL,
AND ENTHRONIZATION OF CHARLES X., KING OF France.

s Cathedral was built in the 12th Century, and is regarded as an exceedingly grand
osing structure. It is rendered still further remarkable as the building long dedicated
remony of Annointing and Consecrating the Kings of France. The picture represents
or, the floor of which, is much admired, being composed of Lozenges of different co-
marble—in the centre stands the Throne on which the Kings of France for ages have
eir successive seats. The picture will undergo the usual gradations of light, and will
pear, when the Enthronization of Charles X. King of France will be presented. The
al will appear illuminated by innumerable wax candles, and decorated in a style of the
orgeous magnificence. Off the throne will be discovered the King in the attitude of
ng his speech to the assembled Nobles and Clergy. The figures will then recede, giv-
ce to the calm appearance of daybreak.

ors open at half-past seven; Exhibition to commence at eight o'clock precisely
ckets, 2s. 6d.; Children half price—to be had at the Bookstore of Messrs. T. Cary
and at the Door of the Theatre.

THEATRE ROYAL, BIRMINGHAM.
FOR THREE NIGHTS ONLY,
MONDAY, WEDNESDAY, & THURSDAY,
APRIL 14, 16, & 17, 1851.
FIRST TIME IN BIRMINGHAM WITH THE HYDRO-OXYGEN LIGHT.
"The best delivered and illustrated Lectures moving."—TIMES, March 14, 1849.

MR. C. POPHAM
F.A.S. (LATE OF WINCHESTER COLLEGE,)
RESPECTFULLY ANNOUNCES A GRAND SUMMARY DISPLAY OF THE

HEAVENS
ILLUSTRATED BY
THIRTY-NINE MOVEABLE TRANSPARENT DIAGRAMS, 200 SQUARE FEET EACH!

INTRODUCTORY ADDRESS.—SCENE.

THE EARTH

A splendid TRANSPARENT GLOBE, to bost in circumference, apparently suspended in Space, surrounded by an Atmosphere, with a magnificent
assemblage of Clouds, as in Nature, the Gorgeous Hues of the Rising Sun. In this, Ships are seen in actual motion, approaching to and departing
from Land, clearly demonstrating the Rotundity of the Earth.
Scene.—The EARTH revolving upon its Axis, bringing the various Continents of EUROPE, ASIA, AFRICA, and AMERICA, Sun-rise, Mid-day,
and Sunset, Eleventh Twilight into Night, the Stars Heavens, and Inverted Moon.
Scene.—The EARTH surrounded by the Zodiacal Sign of the Month, as presented by Clouds in Space, Trades of Stone Globes, each
exhibiting that portion bright which is straight light it is the Sun Stars Sharp Of March again
Scene.—The EARTH in its true position in the ECLIPTIC, to March, June, September, and December, plainly exhibiting the causes of the
SEASONS, or Spring, Summer, Autumn, and Winter, Long and Short Days, &c.
**Probable Causes of the striking Changes now experienced, compared to the Winters and
Summers of 1800, 1814, &c.**

THE SUN, EARTH, AND MOON,
The latter in actual motion round the Earth, and demonstrating to every capacity
HER CHANGES, AND THE CAUSE OF THE EBBING AND FLOWING OF THE TIDES.

THE MOON
AS SEEN THROUGH A NATIONAL TELESCOPE;
Also the most accurately detailed Map in Relievo, displaying the Mountains, Volcanoes, Ridges, &c., on the Lunar Surface, in a most beautiful manner,
by RUSSELL, after 30 Years observation. This Explanation will here be given of the rivers adopted to ascertain the Moon's distance from the
Earth; her Bulk or Magnitude—whether she is inhabited or not, considered.

ECLIPSE OF THE MOON.
The Machinery is combined with Dioramic effect, producing an exact Representation of the total Eclipse which happened January 17th, 1851, visible
at Birmingham. The Moon is seen emerging above the horizon in a beautiful Landscape, 24 feet square, suffering Eclipse as in Nature, the light
fading and brightening as the Planet enters and quits the Earth's shadow.

THE SOLAR SYSTEM—PLANETS, COMETS, AND STARS IN SPACE—THE

SUN
HIS TRUE PHYSICAL CONSTITUTION,—THE CAUSE OF LIGHT AND HEAT.

Scene.—The Planet MERCURY, through a 20-feet glass, 1400 degrees of magnifying power.	Scene.—JUPITER and his FOUR SATELLITES.
Scene.—The Planet VENUS, Diurnal and Annual Motion, her Seasons, &c.	Scene.—SATURN and his SEVEN MOONS; 20-feet Reflector.
Scene.—The Planet MARS, (20-feet Reflector,) Annual and Diurnal Motion, Scenery, and Nature.	Scene.—GEORGIUM SIDUS and SIX MOONS. Scene.—WESTERN ABBEY. COMETS, FIXED STARS. Fully explained. All Rising and Setting as in Nature.

COMETS AND STARS, A
TRANSPARENT ORRERY,
Showing the Heavenly Bodies, suspended in Space, revolving about the Sun.

In conclusion, Mr. MARTIN will exhibit, with appropriate Music, his much admired DISSOLVING

DIORAMA
OF SACRED, CLASSIC, ARCTIC, AND ALPINE SCENERY.

Transformation—Rocks—Rainbow appears—Fireworks at Rome—The Chapel of William Tell, Moonlight—Paris Bridge, near
Genera—The Church of St. Bernard—The Grotto of Bethlehem—Birthplace of Christ—Ruins and Scenes in the Holy Land
Destruction of a Packet Ship at Sea by Fire.—Escape of the Crew on the Raft.

North Polar Regions—Ship, Ice-bound—The Aurora Borealis, and darkness of day, where the Sun does not rise for five mon
—Venetian Colonnade—Three exquisite Moonlight Scenes, in England, Ireland, and Scotland—Underground Church Passag
at Crypt, the oldest in England—Summer and Winter—A Snow Storm ; with other Combinations of Ephemeral Scenic Effects.
FOLLOWED BY

CHROMATROPES
THE WHOLE EXHIBITING 2000 SQUARE FEET OF ILLUMINATED SCENERY.

DOORS OPEN AT HALF-PAST SEVEN, TO COMMENCE AT EIGHT, CONCLUDING AT TEN.
ADMISSION: LOWER BOXES, 2s.; SCHOOL PUPILS, HALF-PRICE—UPPER BOXES, 1s. 6d.; CHILDREN, 1s.
PIT, 1s.; CHILDREN, 6d.—GALLERY, 6d.; ALL AGES.
The Box Office will be open each DAY from One till Three o'Clock.

The Diorama soon surpassed the Panorama as a popular spectacle. An advertisement for Daguerre's Regent's Park Diorama appeared on Shillibert's omnibus, the first London omnibus, in 1829. Of all the Diorama buildings, almost as numerous in capital cities as cinema theatres are today, it is the only one that survives. The façade was designed by Nash; the rotunda and picture emplacements (invisible from the front) were the work of A.C. Pugin and the engineer James Morgan. The word 'Diorama' was originally painted on the facia. The Great Globe, Leicester Square (below), long since destroyed, was a flourishing Diorama when it was photographed in 1855. (69–71)

Dioramic transparencies and optical devices based on the Diorama, sho[w]
the Barnes Museum of Cinematography. The great majority of the im[a]
number of actual Diorama paintings have been destroyed, mostly by fir[e]
toys such as these still give a faint idea of the splendour of the public [e]
tainments. In the corner of the case is a Stereorama (c. 1860) for exhibi[t]
succession of dioramic stereographs viewed in rotation by four spectators s[i]
taneously. In the foreground is a French Polyorama Panoptique, c. 1850,[with]
its accompanying box of coloured lithographs on thin paper with seco[nd]
scenes pasted behind them. The scenes change according to whether the li[ght]

t or transmitted. The instrument on a stand in the centre is a Cosmoramic
oscope, c. 1860. The principle of the machine is the same as that of the
orama Panoptique but photographs are used instead of painted scenes. The
rate stand on the right of the case contains a German 19th century porce-
transparency. When light falls directly onto the picture it presents a plain
e moulded surface. But when illuminated from behind the scene emerges in
chiaroscuro and perspective. The lithograph on the right *L'Arrivée de la
e Victoria à Strasbourg* is seen above by direct and below by transmitted
 (72, 73)

Why does this Man appear to ride in Norfolk?

Why does this man appear over head and ears in debt

Why is this Parrot like a drunken Man!

The cinema was the successor on a cultural level of the spectacles and entertainments illustrated on the preceding pages, but none of these was a true moving picture. Technically the cinema came into being as the result of experiment with a variety of toys based on the phenomenon of persistence of vision. This phenomenon was demonstrated in 1825 by Dr John Ayrton Paris, the inventor of the pretty contrivance shown here, called the Thaumatrope. Strings were attached on either side of a paper disc so that it might be twirled between finger and thumb. Each face of the disc presented a different image, but when it was rotated the images merged into a single coherent picture: a rider mounted his horse, a bald man acquired a wig, a parrot entered his cage. (74, 75)

The Phenakisticope was the first device to show [a con]
vincing moving image; it was invented in 1832 by [Profes]
sor J. A. F. Plateau of Brussels (left) and almost [simul]
taneously by Professor S. Stampfer of Vienna who [called]
his toy the Stroboscope. The invention combined th[e prin]
ciple illustrated by the Thaumatrope with the res[ults of]
experiments conducted by Dr P. M. Roget and Fa[raday]
to demonstrate that the spokes of a rotating wheel [appa]
rently remained stationary when viewed through a [series]
of vertical slots. The edge of a pasteboard disc is n[otched]
to form cogs between which are painted figures in [conse]
cutive positions. The disc is attached to a spin[dle by]
means of nut and screw and rotated rapidly in fr[ont of]
a mirror. The image in the looking glass, viewed th[rough]
the slots performs a series of convincing movemen[ts. In]
the case of the Phenakisticope shown here (the actu[al one]
used by Muybridge when he was experimenting o[n the]
photography of motion) all the wheels revolve. (7[)

The Zoetrope, another toy based on the principle of persistence of vision, was invented by W. G. Horner of Bristol in 1834 although it was not put on the market until 1867. The Zoetrope consists of a slot-pierced drum of metal revolving horizontally on a pivot attached to a heavy base. Each Zoetrope is accompanied by a set of paper bands equal in length to the circumference of the drum and in width to half its depth, and picturing in flat colours, and simple outlines, figures in various stages of a movement. A flat disc is placed on the bottom of the Zoetrope round which again, the consecutive phases of a movement are depicted. When the figures on band and disc are viewed through one of the slots as the drum is rotated, they spring at once into vivid action. (78, 79)

An improvement on the Zoetrope was constructed by
fessor Emile Reynaud (above) and patented in Paris in
It was called the Praxinoscope and was similar in pri
to the Zoetrope except that the slots were abolishec
replaced by rectangular mirrors, set round an inner drum
flect the circling images, all exquisitely drawn and paint
the inventor. The movement exhibited was much sm
and less dazzling than that shown by the Zoetrope. (8

A further advance was made when Reynaud produced h
chanting Praxinoscope Theatre. The flying images reflec
the mirrors of the central drum are viewed through a prosce
between which and the turn table with the drums, are
pieces of scenery which remain stationary while the figur
in full movement. Above and right, a Praxinoscope Th
with picture band of a child playing battledore and sh
cock. Above, the image as seen through the proscenium. (8

The Viviscope (left) was anoth[er]
19th century toy based on the pri[nciple]
demonstrated by the Zoetrope. A[n end-]
less band with phases of a mo[vement]
depicted on it is placed on the [top]
of a drum interrupted by a pil[lared]
proscenium. The band is in conta[ct with]
the drum except where two [?]
rollers are interposed. When the [handle]
is turned the rollers are set in m[otion]
and travel round behind the [band,]
pressing it outwards into the p[rosce-]
nium arch, then returning it to c[ontact]
with the drum, its advance equ[al to]
the width of one picture phas[e.]

BEALE'S CHOREUTOSCOPE

first attempts at projecting the true moving picture were prompted by the
nakisticope. The Ross Wheel of Life (above), patented in 1871, was basically
henakisticope disc adapted for use with the lantern. It consisted of two discs,
opaque, the other bearing the figures. One sector was moved from the opaque
which rotated while the figured disc moved one stage. (86)

Choreutoscope (below), invented by the engineer L. S. Beale in 1866, showed
vement by means of an arrangement, almost identical with the Maltese Cross
vice which was essential to the future development of cinematography, and by
ans of a front shutter to mask each successive phase of the movement. Inter-
tent movement and the shutter action were achieved by means of a circular
c, carrying a pin attached to a handle. As it revolved the pin engaged with a
ch on the slide, moving it on by the space of one picture, and at the same time
sing the shutter. (87, 88)

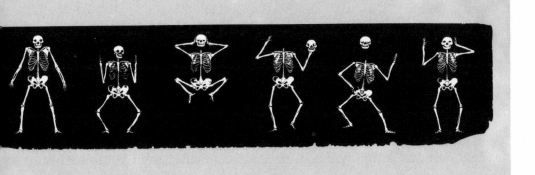

A motion picture projector had already been developed in 1853 by an Austr[ian] army officer, Franz von Uchatius, which combined Phenakisticope discs with [a] lantern. In 1869, A. B. Brown patented a form of Projecting Phenakisticope in [the] United States, which incorporated a form of Maltese Cross movement and a shut[ter]. Brown's machine resembled that shown above, made by the German 'E. P.' C[om]pany *c.* 1890. In the lower example a slotted disc takes the place of the shut[ter]. (89–91)

The magicians with the little black box

In contrast to the excessively complicated prehistory of 'living projections', the story of photography is relatively clear. In fact, the invention itself can be dated to the very year.[1]

In 1727 a German professor named Johann Heinrich Schulze made the chance discovery that objects which he placed in a mixture of silver nitrate and chalk made images of themselves.[2] The next discovery in the chain that led to photography, the production of pictures on paper, was made by Thomas Wedgwood, an Englishman.[3] But real photography, not an impermanent silhouette of an object, but the permanent print of an image from the camera obscura, was offered to the public for the first time on August 19, 1839.

In 1822 Nicéphore Niepce was carrying out experiments which almost brought him to the threshold of the actual invention.[4] In 1826 he heard of similar ventures by the Parisian painter Louis Jacques Mandé Daguerre.[5] On December 14, 1829, both men signed a contract defining the conditions for joint work. But Niepce died four years later. Daguerre, assisted by his son Isidore, carried on the work, utilising all the knowledge gathered by Niepce. After various technical intermediary states (1831 and 1835), he arrived at a procedure which yielded an astonishingly clear picture on a silvered copper plate. These pictures were, to be sure, inverted, and could not be reproduced, but they were achieved with an exposure of only fifteen minutes in sunlight. At the end of 1838 Daguerre demonstrated his invention to Alexander von Humboldt (1769–1859), the naturalist and geographer, and the astronomer and politician François Arago (1786–1853). Arago promptly reported on the discovery to the French Academy of Sciences. The inevitable disputes over priority arose between Daguerre and Niepce's heirs. Such disputes were as customary as they were foolish. Death had taken Niepce too soon; the glory consequently went to the survivor.[6] In June 1839 the French government officially purchased the invention and bestowed a pension of 6000 francs on Daguerre. Niepce's son was accorded a pension of 4000 francs. Although one newspaper commented that the annual maintenance of the monkeys in the Paris Zoo cost more than the pension for this great son of France, the episode remains one of the rare examples of an invention immediately accepted and rewarded by both public and government.

Attacks upon legends are always interesting. The iconoclast need not be right, but he always offers new material. Daguerre has been unquestionably accepted as the father of photography. But now Lo Duca has come along with his book *Bayard* (Paris, 1943) which bears the challenging title 'The first photographic artist'.

Who is this Bayard, whom most of us have never heard of, and what is the basis of this claim for his priority? The evidence

Lo Duca has amassed is fairly formidable. He has dug up twenty-one papers dealing with Bayard. He reproduces forty-nine truly amazing pictures, a facsimile of Bayard's signature, and four portraits of the man by others.

Hippolyte Bayard (1801–1887), son of a judge in Breteuil-sur-Noye, was himself a treasury official in Paris. In 1838 he began making 'photogenic drawings', paper prints, in a dark-room. By February 1839 he was showing them, already con-siderably improved, to numerous friends in Paris. On May 20 he was received by Arago. Arago, however, had already cast his lot in with Daguerre; he was preparing a detailed report on Daguerre, to be delivered to the Academy of Sciences on August 19, and found Bayard's appearance something of a nuisance. He did not visit the exhibition of Bayard's work which opened in the rue des Jeûneurs on June 24, 1839, an ex-hibition consisting largely of genuine photographs. Daguerre's name became identified with photography in general (although his process continued in use for barely fifteen years). In 1851 Bayard received the Cross of the Legion of Honour – but for his services as bureau chief in the Ministry of Finance. He died, completely forgotten as a photographer, in Nemours in 1887.

This unfortunate inventor made his own rather macabre comment on his lot. When it became quite clear that all the glory was going to Daguerre, he made a photograph showing himself as a half-naked, drowned corpse. It was a horrifying picture, with head and hands blackish, discoloured, and an ac-companying text: 'The corpse you see here is that of Monsieur

Bayard, the inventor of the process which has just been shown to you, or whose wonderful results you are going to see. As far as I know, this inventive and indefatigable scientist occupied himself for about three years in perfecting his invention. The Academy, the King, and all those who saw his pictures admired them, as you are doing at this moment, although he himself considered them still defective. This has brought him much honour and not a single sou. The government, which has supported Monsieur Daguerre beyond need, declared itself unable to do anything for Monsieur Bayard, and the unfortunate thereupon cast himself into the river out of despair. Oh, inconstancy of human things! For a long time artists, scientists and the newspapers have concerned themselves with him, and now, though he has been exhibited in the morgue for days, no one has yet recognised him or claimed him.

Ladies and gentlemen, let us pass on to something else, so that your olfactory nerves are not assaulted, for the gentleman's face and hands are already beginning to decay, as you no doubt have observed.'

Another of the major and early contributors to the invention of photography was the English scientist William Henry Fox Talbot.[7] His procedure permitted *any number* of positive prints to be taken on silver-chloride paper. He called the prints Talbotypes and later, for their beauty, Calotypes. Photography thus became a method of multiplication – that is the great importance of this invention. Since film, too, had to be reproducible for the cinema to arise, Talbot's process was in this sense an essential step. In addition, Talbot succeeded in reducing exposure time to three minutes. By 1847 Niepce de Saint Victor (1805–1870), a nephew of Nicéphore, reduced exposure time to three seconds. Sir John Herschel had taken a photograph on glass in 1839 and Niepce de Saint Victor used glass plates instead of paper negatives. But his plates were coated with iodized albumen. In 1851 Frederick Scott Archer invented a method of using a glass plate with a film of wet collodion, which was the first practical process on glass. R. L. Maddox (1816–1902), an English physician, used silver-bromide plates with a gelatine coating as binding agent. These cut exposure time to a hundredth of a second. Meanwhile the wet plate had been replaced by the dry plate, and photography (the first use of the word, incidentally, is attributed both to the German astronomer J. H. von Mädler and to Sir John Herschel) began to conquer the world. It fell into the hands of laymen, and the demands of amateur photographers transformed laboratory experiments into an industry.

In those days the man with the camera was born – the reconnoiterer of reality. Photographs taken between 1840 and 1870[8] were recovered again, despite great difficulties, in the twenties of our century, and carefully collected. The pictures are now regarded as the 'incunabula of photography', and the men who took them are seen as the Rembrandts of the camera. In point of fact these early photographs, especially those by Nadar[9] and by Hill,[10] are remarkable in their own right as works of art. At that time the specific differences between painting and photography were not realized; photographs were taken as an auxiliary to paintings. And no wonder: Anderson, Baldus, Hill, Le Gray, Nègre, and Price were painters by trade, Gagart, Delamotte, and Nadar draughtsmen.

It was also no wonder that the painters of the time, especially the portraitists, looked upon photography as a fiendish form of competition. By 1851 there were fifty-one studios of portrait photographers in New York alone.[11] Caricaturists as great as Honoré Daumier poked fun at the new 'art'. But Victor Hugo, the great French poet, took a camera with him when he went into exile.

There is no doubt that photography ushered in a new way of conquering the world. It was not just a new way of seeing old things, but a way to discover new things.

With the introduction of the first simple cameras, even an idiot, armed with a kodak,[12] could gain revealing glimpses of nature, society, and private relationships such as had been available in the past neither to the secret police, the natural scientists nor the most powerful governments.[13] All anyone needed was the pretext that he 'wanted a record'. It is a significant comment on the trend of the century that from the very beginnings of photography there has been a tendency to discover 'reality' only in the lower strata of society. The first documentary photographs showed 'the world as it really is' by portraying the corpses on the battlefields of the American

Civil War. Mathew Brady, who took those pictures, was a self-made man who probably could not even write, who wavered as to whether his birth date was in 1823 or 1824, and whose tombstone even falsified the date of his death – for he died in 1896, not 1895.[14] Other ardent realists brought pictures home from the Boxer Rebellion: 'Before and after the execution'. The 'after' series of pictures showed how neatly the heads had been severed from the bodies.[15]

The French poet Jean Cocteau, who in a life full of achievements also made some remarkable motion pictures, once spoke of 'stupid registration with the cow-eye of photography'. There is also a much-quoted maxim to the effect that photography must be done not with the hand but with the head. That maxim, however, has little bearing on the actual facts of the photographic industry. Heads are rare.

But we have anticipated; our remarks really apply to a later phase of photography which had ceased to record static, motionless, frozen time, but had become instantaneous photography, 'shooting' genuine, flowing motion. Instantaneous photography is always a segment cut from the Heraclitan flux. Even before instantaneous photography, when long exposures were still necessary, Plateau[16] first hit on the idea of replacing drawn phase-pictures by photographs. (The first persons who projected photographs on glass plates were probably the Langenheim brothers in Philadelphia. The elder brother, Wilhelm, is probably better known for his adventurous life. He came to America in 1834 from Brunswick, Germany. He served in the Texan War of Independence against Mexico, recaptured the Alamo with the American troops, was taken prisoner, condemned to death, and escaped only to fling himself into the war against the Seminole Indians in Florida. Then he decided to join his brother Friedrich and became a photographer).

Given the long exposure time, the various phases of an action had to be posed one by one. With such time-exposures, made on collodion plates and then converted into transparent positives, Henry Heyl[17] projected dance-scenes from his Phasmotrope. But even single instantaneous shots were of little use; what was needed to approach cinematography was the 'series photograph', that is to say, a continuous succession of instantaneous photographs of a movement.[18]

Among the innumerable efforts in that direction,[19] the most fruitful were those of Muybridge and Anschütz: also the experiments of Marey, the French physiologist.

The story goes that a wager between the Governor of California and one of his friends led Eadweard Muybridge to set up his series of cameras.[20] The year was 1877, and the point in dispute was whether a galloping horse ever had all four legs off the ground at the same time. To settle the question, Muybridge stationed twenty-four cameras side by side along a race track. Twenty-four threads were stretched across the track, and as the galloping horse broke these, it tripped the shutters of the cameras. (Later a clockwork device tripped the shutter.)

In 1878 Muybridge was still using wet collodion plates; he changed to dry plates only after 1881. What he achieved were phase pictures of galloping; put together, these made a 'series picture'. Muybridge was an analyst of motion; he never thought initially of using the analysis as a means of later synthesis – in other words, of putting his photographs together into a 'moving picture'. In keeping with this attitude, he used his first series pictures as book illustrations, or presented them in the form of transparent positives in the course of lectures. He was quite unaware that he was doing something momentous when he projected his series of transparent positives in San Francisco in 1879.

The success of his series pictures was international. Muybridge had cut movement into cross-sections, and the science of his day hailed the feat.

The German photographer Ottomar Anschütz heard about Muybridge's experiments soon after they were made, but he did not make his own series pictures until 1884.[21] On the other hand, his pictures compared in quality to those of Muybridge as, to use a modern analogy, a Leica's to a box camera's.

One important advance must indubitably be credited to him. By way of his Tachyscope Viewing Apparatus he arrived at his Electrical Tachyscope. The firm of Siemens built seventy-eight Tachyscopes between 1892 and 1895. A Geissler tube intermittently illuminated each transparent positive as it moved past a slit. From this 'Swift Viewer' for a single person

Anschütz developed an apparatus capable of giving public shows. In 1894 he gave a demonstration at the post office in Berlin throwing his pictures on a screen six by eight meters in size.[22]

A variety of useful experiments were undertaken by Etienne-Jules Marey.[23] A physiologist, he was interested in recording the events in animal and human movements. In considering his work we must distinguish strictly between the fixed plate photographs (chronophotographs) and his strip films.[24] Books on the history of cinema tend to include chronophotography among the decisive discoveries and it was important for the development of photography. On the other hand, the photographic gun Marey introduced in 1882 and with which he took his first chronophotographs, was enormously significant for the 'motion picture'. Twelve photographs per second, taken with the gun, enabled Marey to analyse the movements of a bird in flight. This was achieving genuine series pictures, which he also projected. True, the projections could scarcely have been other than shadowy.[25] But Marey must also be credited with having begun to work with rolls of paper film instead of glass plates in 1887; from 1888 on, he experimented with celluloid film. And that was a great stride forward. Eventually he succeeded in taking up to a hundred pictures a second; and Marey's camera had a great advantage over the apparatus of both, Muybridge and Anschütz – it was portable.

At this point, and probably for the first time, the development of picture-making intersects with that of picture-projecting in a manner which makes it impossible to decide which line of evolution led to the making of the first 'film' – namely, that celluloid strip which much later would give its name to a greater whole. We may regard an American, Hannibal Goodwin,[26] as the inventor; but then again, it was an American, George Eastman, who though not its originator[27] was its greatest promoter – with his roll film. In 1888 he invented the Kodak. He used the profits from it for large-scale philanthropy: by 1925 he had given some fifty-eight million dollars for charitable and especially educational purposes. On March 14, 1932, he drew up his will in regard to the remainder of the fortune, and after his lawyers had left, he shot himself.

Eastman, who was devoted purely to photography, had not made his invention with any notions about cinematography in mind. The connection was established by W. Laurie Dickson, the associate of Thomas Alva Edison (1847–1931), the Wizard of Menlo Park.[28] It is one of the curiosities of technology that Edison, when he requested 'film', was not working on cinematography at all; he was merely thinking of an improvement to his phonograph (which he later renamed 'gramophone'). He had already learned how to preserve sounds and language, and he now wanted to supplement them by pictures.[29]

Edison was in a different class from the men named so far, whose accomplishments seem paltry beside his. We would probably be justified in calling Edison the last technical genius, the last of the great solitary inventors, who flourish only so long as a given technology can still be surveyed as a whole. But even in his case, the little experimenter's shack of his early years soon expanded into a laboratory. Thus the product of individual genius was transformed into the laboratory invention, the group invention of today. Nowadays processes are worked out not by inventors, but by teams under the guidance of a research director, and the results are no longer attached to the names of individuals. Indeed, key portions of the cinema apparatus were developed in the Edison laboratory while Edison himself was off travelling in Europe.

In 1888 the first cinema camera was ready; on October 6, 1889, the first projection took place (only as a laboratory experiment). Shortly afterwards, the Edison laboratory began making brief story film strips. These no longer consisted of series pictures – a circuit of pictures which returned on themselves – but continuous pictures, genuine segments of life in motion. In April 1891 Edison applied for patents on the Kinetograph as a photographing camera and the Kinetoscope as a viewing apparatus.[30] He set up a special studio in which he installed a camera which was already movable, though confined to rails, and produced films of up to six hundred individual frames. He perforated his film strips with four holes per frame (a detail which is taken for granted today, but which was something that only Le Prince, a Frenchman working in England, had attempted). Neat perforation was a genuine and vital improvement; thanks to it, the frames could be kept equidistant and moving smoothly. Indeed, Edison's perforations set the standard of size for film which has remained the norm.

The Kinetoscope, the most advanced cinematographic viewing apparatus to be developed up to that time, became a worldwide success.[31] Edison owed some ideas to Muybridge, Marey, Anschütz, and Eastman, but those who followed along this course owed more to him. No unworldly visionary, but a man who knew how to transform inventions into industries, Edison clearly saw what the next task must be. The viewing apparatus had to be changed into a projection apparatus. But after a certain amount of tinkering, he shelved the project. By the time he went back to it, the Lumière brothers had beaten him to the goal.

Notes to the text

1 General surveys in J. W. Eder: *Geschichte der Photographie* (Halle, 1932); B. Newhall: *The History of Photography from 1839 to the Present Day* (New York, 1949); L. Moholy: *A Hundred Years of Photography* (Harmondsworth, 1939); E. Stenger: *Siegeszug der Photographie* (Seebruck, 1950). All these works contain numerous documents. For specialised works see Bibliography.

2 1687–1744. Professor of Anatomy and Surgery. He was also a teacher of geography, botany and philology, a famous numismatist and expert in both Greek and Arabic. He made positive and negative prints, but did not discover how to 'fix' them.

3 1771–1805. Together with Sir Humphrey Davy, 1802: *Report on a Method for the Production of Silhouettes by the Influence of Light on Silver Nitrate*. But these pictures, too, could not be fixed so that they were lightfast.

4 1765–1833. Started as a student of theology, then became an army officer, then an inventor – if that may be called an occupation. After exposures of many hours he obtained camera obscura images on light-sensitive metal plates. The process, developed from lithography and heliography, did not produce real photographs, but only printed plates.

5 1787–1851. Daguerre already had a name as the inventor of the Diorama. His most important publication: *Historique et description des procédés du daguerréotype et du diorama.*

6 For details on the relationship of Niepce and Daguerre, see Fouqué: *La Vérité sur l'invention de la photographie* (Paris, 1867).

7 1800–1877. Botanist, mathematician and physicist. On January 31, 1839, he presented to the Royal Society: *The Process of Calotype Photogenic Drawing.* His *The Pencil of Nature,* 1844, was the first photographic picture book.

8 See Bossert and Guttmann: *Aus der Frühzeit der Photographie* (Frankfurt, 1930).

9 Gaspar Félix Tournachon, called Nadar (1820–1910), physician, balloonist, journalist, caricaturist – a bohemian. See: *Quand j'étais Photographe* (Paris, 1899).

10 David Octavius Hill (1801–1870), lithographer, illustrator, landscape painter. In 1843 four hundred and seventy-four ministers protested against the National Church of Scotland and demanded a Free Church. Hill pledged himself to paint the dramatic scene of the Disruption. In order to be able to incorporate four hundred and seventy-four portraits in a colossal painting, he called upon the services of a 22-year-old calotypist named Robert Adamson. English portrait photography was born.

11 Stenger, op. cit., reproduces a precious collection of contemporary comments.

12 Kodak advertisement: 'You press the button, we do the rest.' Incidentally the slogan is given first place by J. L. Watkins in *The 100 Greatest Advertisements* (New York, 1959).

13 The wholly new relationship between parents and children created by the cabinet photograph, and between individual and state created by the passport pictures, is a matter that has not yet been adequately investigated by sociologists.

14 J. D. Horan: *Mathew Brady, Historian with a Camera* (New York, 1955).

15 Stenger, op. cit., Plate 57.

16 In 1849. By then Plateau had been completely blind for five years.

17 On February 5, 1870, at the Young Men's Society of Saint Mark's Evangelical Church in Philadelphia. Later technical improvements were made by Le Roy.

18 Breaking up a circular movement, with the aid of series photography, for example, corresponds to construction of a circle out of an infinite-sided polygon. To conceive of nature in quanta is the summit of technical thinking.

19 By Claudet, Irving, Sutton, Ducos du Hauron, Janssen and others. To adjudicate the share each nation has had in the development is matter for a special study – but one hardly worth making.

20 'Official Photographer for the US Government for the Pacific Coast.' The 'picture sequences' were made by a series of cameras arranged in a row, not by a single camera

taking pictures in sequences. With his Zoopraxinoscope he projected both the original picture sequences and drawings made from them. The principle was that of the Phenakisticope.

21 Anschütz (1846–1907) was also inventor of the slot shutter. He too used series of cameras, twelve to fourteen, but built into a single framework.

22 These projections are extremely important for the prehistory of the cinema (see Traub, p. 33 ff.). He began them on November 25, 1894, using a double projector (eight picture phases in each, a total of sixteen!) and showed amusing scenes, such as a barber soaping a man's face. Above all, these were public performances; admission was charged of between 1 and 1.50 marks. While Muybridge had only improved the Phenakisticope for his projections, Anschütz with his double projector set out on a new – though wrong – road.

23 1830–1904. Professor of physiology in Paris. *La Photographie du Mouvement* (1892) and *La Chronophotographie* (1899).

24 By repeated flashes of light he retained on a *single* plate the various phases of movement – for example, of a fencer's lunge or a man's step. Such plates could not be used for projection. He himself deprecated his share in the invention of Chronophotography in *Le Mouvement* (1889) where he ascribed 'l'honneur d'avoir inauguré' entirely to the astronomer Janssen (1824–1917), who in 1873 had con-

structed the *révolver photographique* and a year later had used the instrument in Japan to photograph the transit of Venus. Marey's photographic gun was a development of this camera.

25 His work was directly carried on by Georges Demeny (1850–1917), who in 1892 by means of his Phonoscope projected the first close-up of a face articulating the words, 'Je vous aime' – in such a manner that a deaf-mute could lip-read the words. By his patents of October 10, 1893 (N° 233,337), and of July 27, 1894, by his invention of the Chronotograph (which, however, did not go into production until the end of 1895, after Lumière's shows), he went beyond his teacher, Marey, and came very close to duplicating Lumière's invention. See Sadoul, *Histoire,* vol. I, p.156 ff.

26 1822–1900. Clergyman. As early as 1887 he tried to obtain a patent for celluloid as a base for a light-sensitive emulsion. The invention lay in the combination. Goodwin did not invent strips (they had already been tried, though made of different material), nor celluloid (an American Celluloid Company had been founded in 1870; first important patent: U.S.P. 91,341, by Hyatt, dated June 15, 1869). Hyatt had invented celluloid while trying to find a substitute for ivory billiard balls, demand for which had risen enormously.

27 1854–1932. Founded a photographic factory by 1880. Immediately exploited his adaptation of celluloid film

(Eastman-Walker patents U.S.P. 358,845 of October 25, 1884, and U.S.P. 420,130 of June 27, 1884, also Eastman patent U.S.P. 471,469 of August 3, 1889). This led to the first of the great patent infringement suits in cinema history – between Goodwin and the Eastman Kodak Company. In 1898 the suit was decided in favour of Goodwin, but the disputes over claims continued until 1914.

28 Detailed account in the book by the co-inventor, Dickson: *History of the Kinematograph, Kinetoscope and Kinetophonograph* (London, 1895).

29 According to a letter in 'Nature', the idea of combining the two already occurred to Wordsworth Donisthorpe in 1878.

30 Important patents dated August 24, 1891: U.S.P. N°s 493,426 and 589,168.

31 In the literature of cinematography and even in professional journals, especially in picture captions, I have frequently found the Kinetoscope confounded with the Mutoscope. These have nothing in common except the external form of the viewing apparatus. The Mutoscope, manufactured from 1895 on, did in fact show continuous photographs; but these were exhibited on the principle of the 'flicker books' (known since 1868): phase pictures on postcards, bound in book form, which created an illusion of movement when rapidly leafed through. In the Mutoscope these 'postcards' are arranged on a horizontal axis which can be turned by a hand crank after a coin is dropped into the slot. The Mutoscope is undoubtedly the most stable of all early

cinematographic devices. Sadoul notes with respect that in 1939 he found a number of workable models at an exhibition. In 1962 no less than five of the original Mutoscopes were in daily use at Reeperbahn 77–79 in Hamburg. They showed: *Once upon a Time; Yes, Yes, Love is Blind; The Mouse at a Tea Party; The Interrupted Rendezvous* and *When Women Become Hyenas.* And in 1963 I saw original Mutoscopes on Broadway in New York, and at Coney Island – with film titles of which at least a few might have been modern!

The invention of photography and the discovery of method analysing and reconstituting the successive phases of movem photographically are essential to the development of cinema graphy. *Nadar élevant la Photographie à la hauteur de l'.* Caricature by Daumier, 1862, of Nadar, who initiated ae photography by taking pictures from a balloon. (92)

The photographic camera represents the combination of two distinct phenomena, one optical, the other chemical. The optical principle is that of the *camera obscura* (above), an enclosed chamber with an aperture or lens on one side such that a reduced and inverted image of any object within the range of the aperture is flung upon the opposite wall within. The camera obscura was known as early as the fifteenth century. During the eighteenth century both professional and amateur painters made use of it for landscape drawing. By 1835 Henry Fox Talbot had already produced a negative of a window at his home, Lacock Abbey by means of his camera obscura (right). Far right, two of Talbot's Calotype cameras. (93, 94)

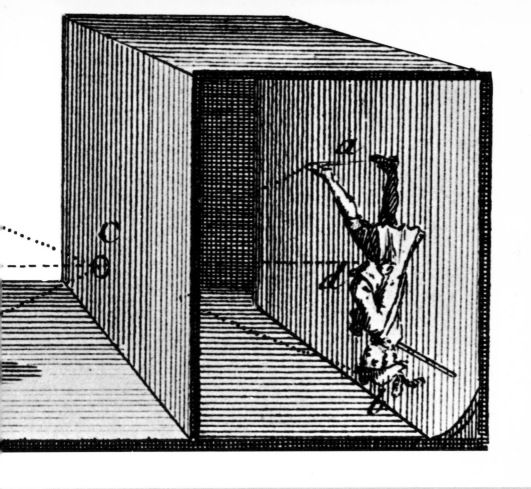

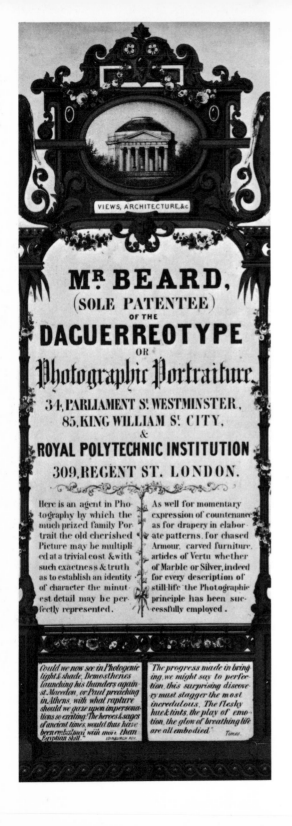

In 1839 L. J. M. Daguerre (right cen[tre],
inventor of the Diorama, succeeded in [pro]-
ducing a picture on a silvered copperp[late]
which was rich in detail and clearly defi[ned].
The use of his method spread like wildfir[e]
over Europe and America, becoming ind[eed]
Daguerreomania. The first public studi[o in]
London was erected on the roof of the R[oyal]
Polytechnic Institution in 1841 by Ric[hard]
Beard, one of whose trade cards (1842[) is]
shown here. (95, 97)

The compound invention of photogra[phy]
was the work not only of Daguerre (cen[tre])
and Talbot (top right) but of Nicép[hore]
Niepce (top left) who obtained pictures [on]
metal, called heliographs between 1816 [and]
1829. The neglected Hippolyte Bayard [(self-]
portrait, below) working without knowle[dge]
of Daguerre and Talbot, produced posi[tive]
photographs on paper in the camera obs[cura]
in 1839. Frederick Scott Archer (below [left])
was the inventor in 1851 of the collo[dion]
or glass plate process. In 1871 Dr Ric[hard]
Maddox (below right) discovered the [dry]
plate process without which the roll f[ilm]
essential to cinematography could not h[ave]
been manufactured. (96, 98–101)

Talbot's Process divulged to the Royal Society in the same year, 1839, as the announcement of Daguerre's discovery, was completely different from the Frenchman's method. Daguerre produced a single image which could not be repeated while Talbot provided a paper negative from which any number of copies could be made on paper. Talbot's Calotypes were the forerunners of modern photographs. Above, Talbot (centre) at work in his photographic establishment at Reading. Right, a Calotype paper negative by Talbot. (102, 103)

To secure a pleasing Portrait is everything.—

...guerreotypist, to cheerful Sitter: "The process will commence
...soon as I lift up this slide. You will have the goodness to look
...edly at one object and call up a pleasant expression to your
...ntenance."

The lengthy exposures which the Daguerreotype process entailed (4 to 7 minutes in
the sun and from 12 to 60 minutes in diffused
light) necessitated a head rest for the sitter
and gave rise to numerous gibes such as the
caricature by Cuthbert Bede, 1855. (104)

From left to right: The only kn...
guerreotype signed by Daguer...
perhaps of Charles Arrowsmith. ...
Daguerreotype by Beard and a ...
reotype of Edgar Allan Poe by S. W...
horn, 1842. (105–107)

, Calotype of John Murray c. 1845
O. Hill, the greatest exponent of
's method, and two early examples
wet plate process (which reduced
re to 10 to 15 seconds). Sir John
el by Julia Margaret Cameron and
Bernhardt by Nadar. (108–111)

el took the earliest photograph on glass in 1839.
ws Sir William Herschel's 40 ft telescope before
ition. (112)

The subject matter and compo
of early photographs already
shadow the themes and methods
film maker. The studied symmetr
minute treatment of Biow's Da
reotype of the Hahn family *c.*
and the carefully contrived stil
1854, and the posed group o
Prince of Wales and Prince Λ
with their tutor Dr Becker, bo
Roger Fenton, are as significan
later developments as the casua
atmospheric effects of Talbot's *F*
on the Lawn at Lacock and I
Hill's *Finlay Children* and
Friars' Churchyard, Edinburgh
Calotypes. (113–118)

When working out of doors, the photographer using the collodion method had to take with him a complete coating and developing outfit together with a collapsible 'dark tent' carried either in a pack on his back or in a wheelbarrow. (119)

Panoramic views and montage both of which play a large part in film making were very soon attempted by enthusiastic photographers. *The View of Paris* by Friedrich von Martens taken from the Louvre in 1846 with a panoramic camera of his own invention is in reverse as was the case with all early Daguerreotypes. For his *Landscape c.* 1860, C. Silvy combined two negatives, one of the river scene, the other of the sky. (120, 121)

The use of painted backgrounds and acce
in portrait photography reduced the subjec
stage figure. Above, an advertisement for
backgrounds such as were common in profe
journals after 1860, and an early instance
use of painted backgrounds in a Daguerreot
a dancer by C. F. Stelzner, c. 1850 (122, 123)

Combination photography is further exem
by H. P. Robinson's *Fading Away* right to
posite), 1858, produced by using three neg
one showing the foreground group and the cu
the second the background with the figure sta
with his face towards it, the third the sky. O. C
lander's study of Gustave Doré is characteri
the tendency during the second half of the la
tury to dramatize the photographic portrait.
125)

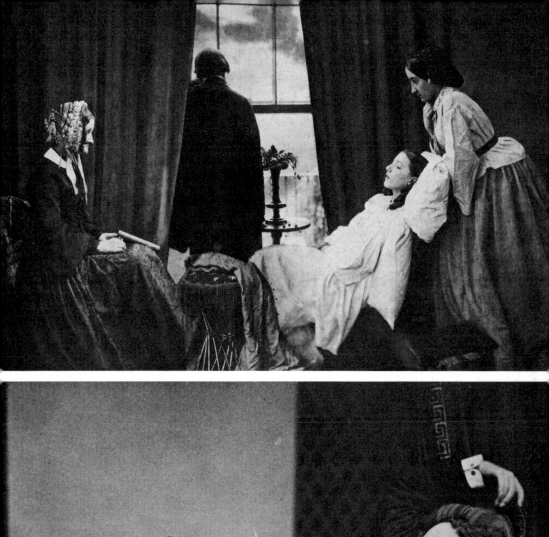

The earliest news photographs, forerunners of news and d
mentary films, were the remarkable Daguerreotypes take
Biow and Stelzner of the ruins of the Alster district of Ham
(above) after the great fire of 1842. Right, the opening of
Crystal Palace at Sydenham, June 10th 1854 by Queen
toria and the Prince Consort, Calotype by an unknown pho
rapher, described as the 'first press photograph'. (126, 127)

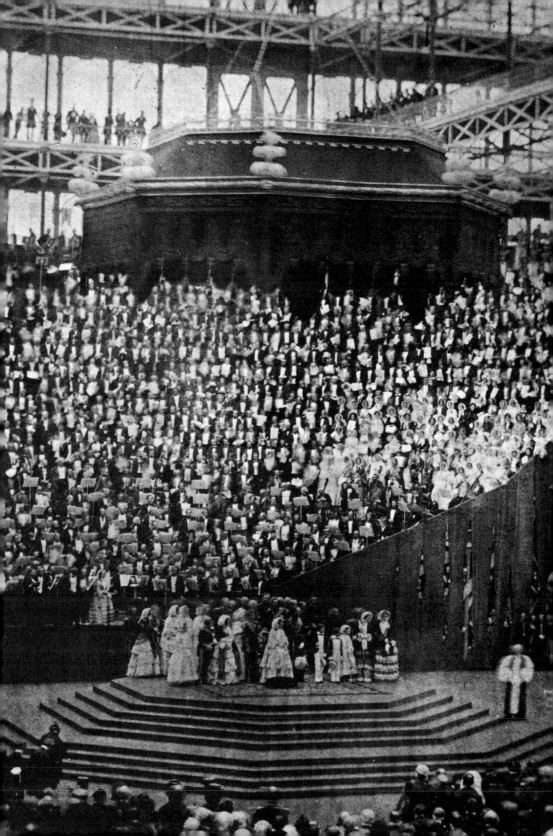

War photographs were first taken in the Crimea (1854–55). Roger Fenton went out to the battlefield in a van with a wet-plate outfit and darkroom tent (above). Below, his photographs of Lt. Gen. Sir George Brown and staff, a cantinière and (right) an evocative study, *The Valley of the Shadow of Death*. (128–131)

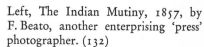

Left, The Indian Mutiny, 1857, by F. Beato, another enterprising 'press' photographer. (132)

Nadar's astonishing picture of the catacombs of Paris, 1860, was one of the first documentary as distinct from topical news photographs. He used a home-made electric light outfit taking advantage of the 'photogenic' quality of the heaps of bones. (133)

The Stereoscope gives the ill[usion of]
depth as in 3 D. films by presen[ting]
slightly dissimilar pictures to the [eyes]
and blending them into a single [one. It]
was invented by Sir Charles W[heatstone]
in 1838. In 1848 Sir David Bre[wster in-]
troduced a binocular camera f[or photo-]
graphing stereoscopic pictures. [Above,]
stereoscopic photographs. Below, [a pedes-]
tal stereoscope, 1885, with pho[tographs]
one of which shows a stereosco[pe. Right,]
and Kilburn's stereoscope of [1888. In]
1852 Wheatstone invented a kin[ematic]
device (right) using strips of ste[reoscopic]
photographs mounted on a d[isc and]
viewed through a lenticular ste[reoscope.]
The principle was similar to th[at of the]
Zoetrope and there was no shu[tter. The]
pictures were each prepared from [separate]
negatives and the resulting move[ment was]
jerky and unconvincing. Nea[rly forty]
years later, in 1889 Friese-Gr[eene and]
Mortimer Evans patented a ste[reoscopic]
cine-camera (below right) to ta[ke stereo-]
scopic images 3 inches square, [but it]
was unable to produce a true mo[ving pic-]
ture effect. (134–140)

Photographic lantern slides were unknown until about 1850 when they were first produced
the brothers W. and F. Langenheim of Philadelphia. They were used to project narrative sequen
based on popular songs and tales and were the immediate forerunners of narrative films.

des were hand coloured and usually showed live models posed against painted backgrounds. ney made use of montage and flashbacks as the cinema was to do. Left, a scene from *The Scent of e Lilies;* above, a scene from *Ora Pro Nobis,* the subject later of a film by R. W. Paul. (141, 142)

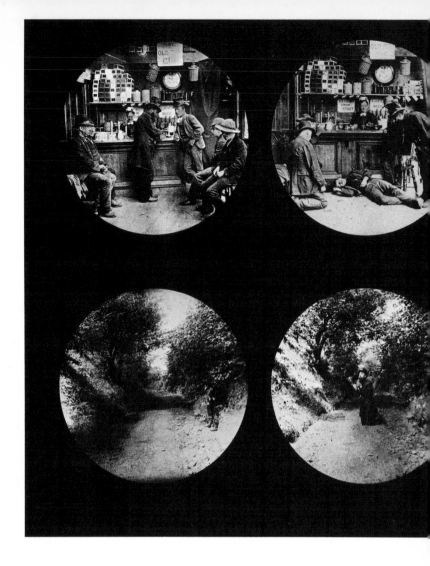

The actors who posed for the photographic narrative slides were not profes
sionals but nameless local people. Occasionally, however, they graduated from
lantern slide to celluloid. When Joseph Bamforth, the maker of the slides in
which they figure, took up cinematography in 1899, the hero of *The Drunkard's
Return* (above), his wife and the child appearing in the last two slides, all took
part in the film *The Gipsy's Revenge*. They are seen in the slides on the right
made from stills of this film. (143–152; 153, 154)

Movement had now to be imparted to the projected image to a
the next step in the development of cinematography. The projec
vented in 1875 (left) by J. A. Roebuck Rudge embodied an interr
mechanism similar to that of modern movie machines and sho
sequence of seven slides revolving round the lamp-house. The
photographs showed different phases of a single movement as c
sequences of eighteen posed photographs (four of which are seen
taken by Henry Heyl and imperfectly projected in Philadelp
1870 by means of the Projecting Phenakisticope. (155, 156)

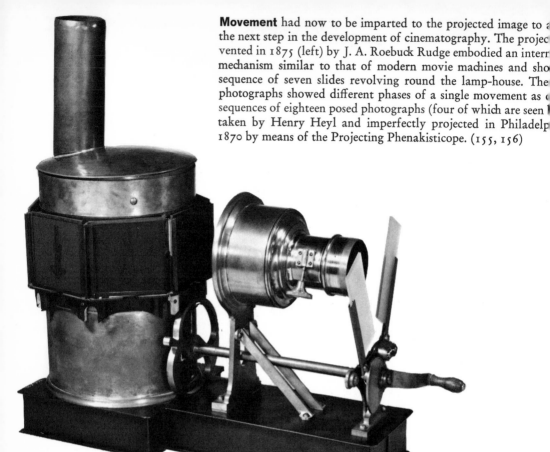

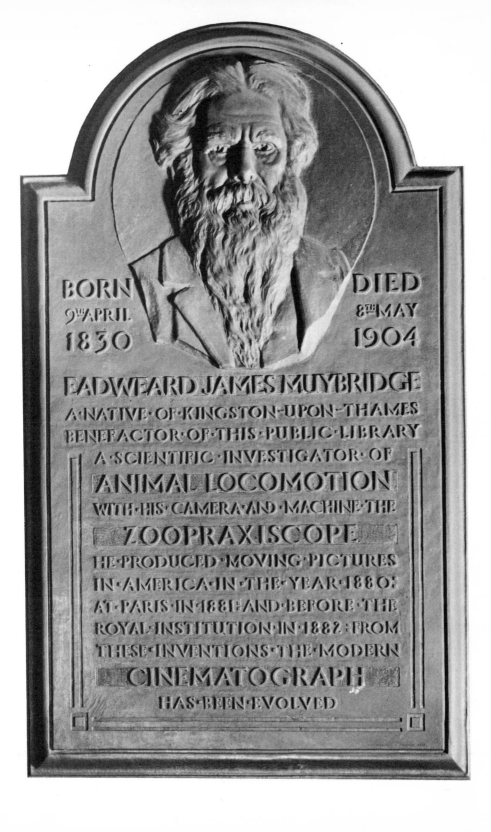

BORN
9TH APRIL
1830

DIED
8TH MAY
1904

EADWEARD JAMES MUYBRIDGE
A·NATIVE·OF·KINGSTON·UPON·THAMES
BENEFACTOR·OF·THIS·PUBLIC·LIBRARY
A·SCIENTIFIC·INVESTIGATOR·OF
ANIMAL·LOCOMOTION
WITH·HIS·CAMERA·AND·MACHINE·THE
ZOOPRAXISCOPE
HE·PRODUCED·MOVING·PICTURES
IN·AMERICA·IN·THE·YEAR·1880:
AT·PARIS·IN·1881·AND·BEFORE·THE
ROYAL·INSTITUTION·IN·1882:FROM
THESE·INVENTIONS·THE·MODERN
CINEMATOGRAPH
HAS·BEEN·EVOLVED

The successful projection of moving photographic images could only be achieved when movement had been analysed into many more phases than was possible with long exposures and individually posed pictures. Eadward Muybridge, one among several scientists working to this end, projected photographic sequences of animals in motion in 1880 by means of his Zoopraxiscope (left), a machine based on the principles of the Projecting Phenakisticope. Below, Muybridge's photographic sequences of a cat and a cart horse. (157–160)

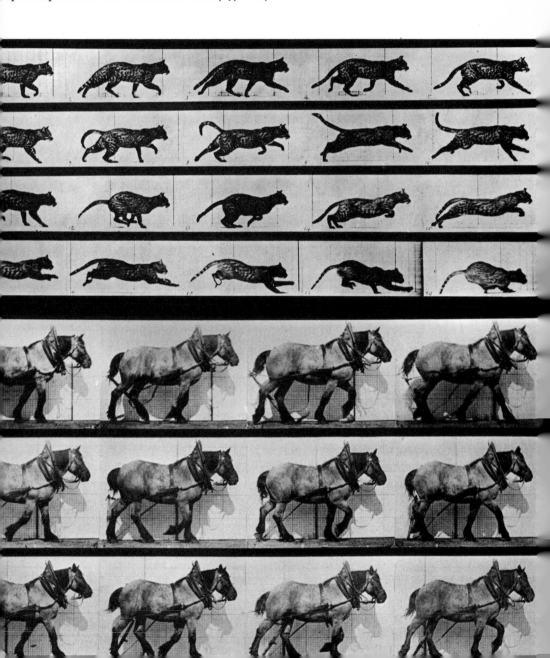

Muybridge's device for taking photographs in rapid succession consisted of a battery of cameras, the shutters of which were released in turn by wires attached to the cameras and pulled down by the animals as they passed. His first attempts were made with wet plates between 1872 and 1897 at Palo Alto, California. Between ten and thirty cameras were used and Muybridge's subjects were men and horses. In 1883–1884 Muybridge began using

dry plates, forty cameras, a Dallmeyer lens and an electric-magnetic shutter; in 1886 he turned from the photography of animals to that of human beings. To this period belong the sequences of the athlete and dancer shown here. Muybridge projected many of his sequences at the Chicago Fair in 1893 in a specially constructed building of classical design, the Zoo-praxographical Hall, a forerunner of the Cinema theatre. (161–164)

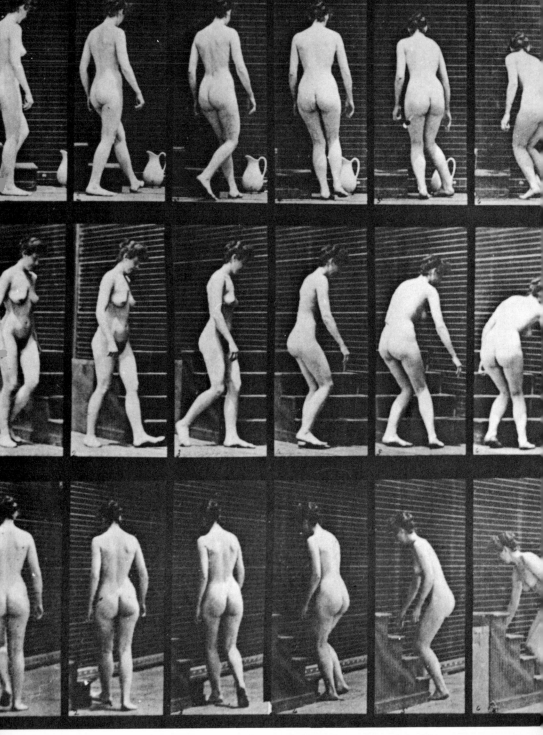

Three sequences by Muybridge of a nude model picking up a jug and asce
ing a flight of steps, from *The Human Figure in Motion*, first published 1901.
help in the analysis of the photographs, a kind of graph was painted on

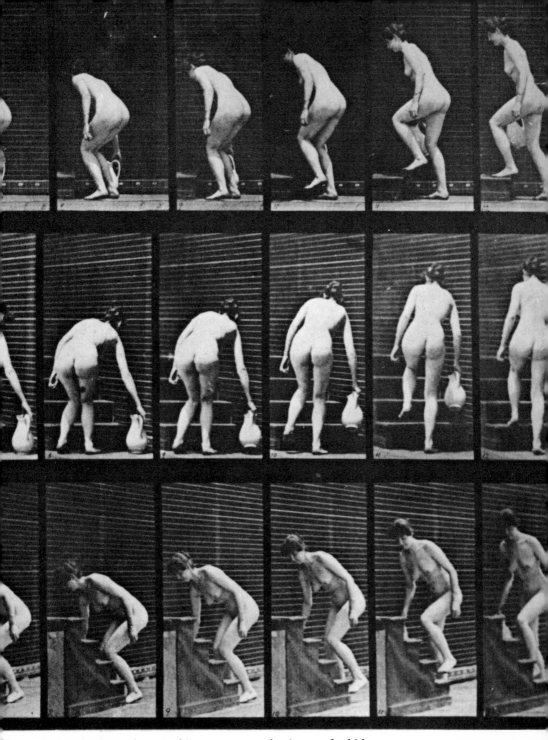

kgrounds. Muybridge's photographic sequences, each picture of which was
en with a separate camera, constituted the consecutive frames of a moving
ture. (165)

The first portable motion picture camera was designed by the physiologist E. J. Marey. It was a rifle shaped camera (shown here in engravings from Marey's 'Movement', 1882), which overcame the great disadvantage of Muybridge's method, the necessity of using a large number of stationary cameras. It took twelve exposures on one plate. In 1888 Marey produced a new 'chronophotographic' camera using rolls of paper film instead of glass plates, which took a series of forty pictures. (166 to 168)

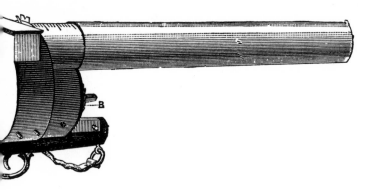

Marey and his achievements are shown on the reverse of a medallion by Paul Richer. It was struck in 1912 to raise funds for the Marey monument. (169)

Chronophotograph by Marey analysing the movement of an athle[te]
1882. The multiple images are all taken on a fixed plate with an eff[...]

is immediately reminiscent of effects seen on the cinema screen,
cially of 'slow motion'. (170)

Chronophotograph by Marey
of a fencer on a fixed plate and
sequence of a falling cat on a
paper roll film. (171, 172)

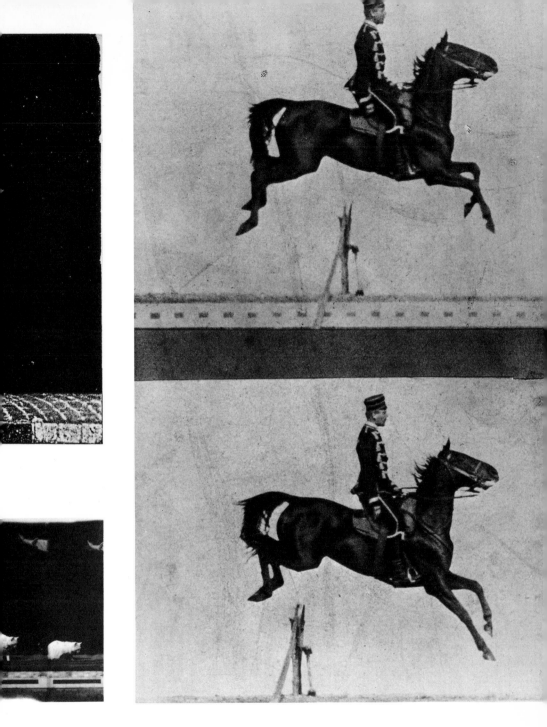

Another pioneer who successfully analysed movement was Ottomar
Anschütz. His pictures, taken from 1882 onwards, were outstanding
for their sharpness, but owing to his persistent use of glass plates the
number of exposures was limited. (173)

Anschütz recomposed his photographic sequences into the original movement by me
of his Tachyscope, 1887. The system was a development of the Zoetrope with
cylinder mounted on a horizontal axis. A little later, in 1889, Anschütz constructed
Electrical Tachyscope, a viewing apparatus for a series of twenty-four photographic ima
successively illuminated by a spiral Geissler tube. This device was the progenitor
modern stroboscopic photography. The Electrical Tachyscope was shown at the Chic
Fair in 1893 and stimulated experiment in the projection of moving pictures. Right
'penny in the slot' Electric Tachyscope built the German firm Siemens. (174, 175)

Elektrischer Schnellseher.

System Anschütz.

SIEMENS & HALSKE

Leihgabe des Reichspostmuseums

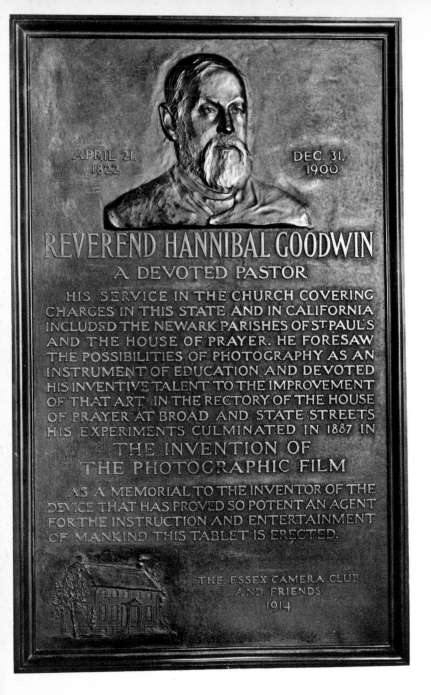

APRIL 21,
1822

DEC. 31,
1900

REVEREND HANNIBAL GOODWIN
A DEVOTED PASTOR
HIS SERVICE IN THE CHURCH COVERING
CHARGES IN THIS STATE AND IN CALIFORNIA
INCLUDED THE NEWARK PARISHES OF ST·PAUL'S
AND THE HOUSE OF PRAYER. HE FORESAW
THE POSSIBILITIES OF PHOTOGRAPHY AS AN
INSTRUMENT OF EDUCATION AND DEVOTED
HIS INVENTIVE TALENT TO THE IMPROVEMENT
OF THAT ART. IN THE RECTORY OF THE HOUSE
OF PRAYER AT BROAD AND STATE STREETS
HIS EXPERIMENTS CULMINATED IN 1887 IN
THE INVENTION OF
THE PHOTOGRAPHIC FILM
AS A MEMORIAL TO THE INVENTOR OF THE
DEVICE THAT HAS PROVED SO POTENT AN AGENT
FOR THE INSTRUCTION AND ENTERTAINMENT
OF MANKIND THIS TABLET IS ERECTED.

THE ESSEX CAMERA CLUB
AND FRIENDS
1914

The use of celluloid as an emulsion base, an essential step in the development of cinematography, was introduced in 1887 by Hannibal Williston Goodwin, an Episcopalian minister who had become interested in photography through the magic lantern entertainments he gave for his congregation. (176)

The first text book on cinematograph the cover of which appears opposite, w written jointly with his sister by W. K. Dickson in 1895. He was chiefly respo sible for the work on the motion pictu done at the Edison laboratory. (177)

HISTORY of the KINETOGRAPH KINETOSCOPE and KINETO-PHONOGRAPH

BY
W. K. L. DICKSON
and
ANTONIA DICKSON

Copyrighted and Designed by
W. K. L. DICKSON.

70, OXFORD STREET, W., LONDON.

Edison's Kinetoscope viewing apparatus w
completed in 1891, the result of experiments
produce motion pictures in combination with t
Phonograph, invented 1877, and shown here wi
Edison himself. The Kinetoscope was a peepsho
in which fifty-foot loops of film could be seen
individual viewers. Right, the first film studio, t
Black Maria, constructed by W. K. L. Dickson
1894, and the shooting of a film for the combin
Kinetoscope and Phonograph in the Black Mar
(178–181)

first Kinetoscope Parlour (above) was
~~ed~~ at 1155 Broadway New York City
~~1~~894 by a Canadian showman, Andrew
~~land~~, who had acquired ten peep-hole
~~vi~~ers from Edison's agents, Raff and
~~Si~~mon. Among the films shown was Dick-
~~s~~ *Record of a Sneeze* (left) showing Fred
~~~~ a laboratory mechanic. (182, 183)

Casler's Mutoscope was yet anot form of peepshow in which photographica analysed movement was reconstituted. series of photographs of successive phases an animated scene are mounted radially an axle. When the axle is rotated each pho graph is held under the lens for an inst and then rapidly replaced by the next. principle of 'persistence of vision' brings scene to life as the viewer peers through lens. In the 1890's Mutoscope Parlours w set up all over America and machines still be seen on the piers of some seas resorts. (184, 185)

The Filoscope patented by Short in 189 a similar contrivance; successive photogra are mounted one behind another upor metal lever, which, when pressed downwa releases the images in turn from a project on the framework. The German film pior Max Skladanowsky had a partiality 'flicker-books' which he made himself on principle of the Mutoscope. (186)

The first film strips

It would satisfy our sense of completeness if we could make a chronological list of all the people who contributed to the development of cinema during the crucial ten years before 1905. But there are too many of them. Moreover, we would find it hard to assign priorities because this period is a jumble of true inventions, clever ideas of secondary importance, incomplete devices, imitations and direct plagiarisms. Besides, before a great invention comes into being, the flying sparks of knowledge charge many minds with the same high tension, and the discharges tend to get out of control. But certainly three men cannot be passed over, since they succeeded several years before Lumière in producing certain types of cinematographic performances whose value as sensations (that is, in their effect on the first spectators) probably equalled that of Lumière's work. In addition, we find in the life and work of these men that note of drama which seems appropriate to the careers of inventors.

Louis Aimé Augustin Le Prince (also called Louis Edmée Auguste Le Prince, 1842–1890), who had studied at Leipzig, subsequently became a director of exhibitions, and a wanderer between Paris, London, Leeds, New York and Chicago, spent the years from 1886 to 1888 developing a camera and projector with sixteen lenses. In his patent statement dated January 10, 1888,[1] he described – and he was certainly the first to do this – separate devices for taking pictures and for projection. In October 1889 in Leeds he tried out a camera with a single lens. By then he was working with celluloid film rather than with the glass plates he had been using previously, and possibly on this occasion he also succeeded in making his first 'film' projections. As early as the winter of 1888–1889 he had begun construction of a device which was to use perforated film and a Maltese Cross gearing.[2] Early in 1890 he took pictures in Paris for the purpose of projection (five years before Lumière), and showed them to several officials of the Paris Opera.[3]

This man, who came within a hair's breadth of inventing cinematography by combining its essential elements, visited his brother in Dijon in September 1890. He boarded the train to return to Paris – and from that moment on disappeared without a trace. Neither his body nor his baggage were ever found. His disappearance remains to this day one of the riddles of criminology, and is really worth a film itself. There is no doubt that destiny cut a thread in this case – for it may be assumed that Le Prince would have perfected his apparatus before five years were out, and thus become the uncontested winner of the race.

Less disjointed and mysterious, but crossed by innumerable frustrations, was the life and work of William Friese-Greene.[4] His name was originally Willie Green; but he added on the name of his German wife and an extra *e* for distinction – one of those minor acts which are useful to a biographer.

Friese-Greene began by adding some ideas of his own to the Biophantascope of John Arthur Roebuck Rudge. A camera that he built between 1885 and 1889 exhibited some of the properties which were later to prove important, but it took pictures at a relatively slow speed, only four to five a second, and these were intended to be cut up, printed and mounted as lantern slides for use in the Rudge-type lantern. In 1888, however, Friese-Greene was in Paris and discovered celluloid. In 1889, working with Mortimer Evans, he produced and patented a camera (patent N° 10,131) but there is no proof that it was ever used for successful projection. His third camera, produced in 1893 (patent N° 22,954) closely resembled that of F.H. Varley whose camera and projector had been patented three years previously. Friese-Greene is said to have given a demonstration before the Bath Photographic Society on February 25, 1890, but the reports of the meeting on that date prove that no projection took place. There is also no evidence that he wrote to Edison giving detailed drawings of an apparatus combining the phonograph with his camera and receiving only a cool acknowledgement from Edison's office in reply. The underlying assumption that the American had filched his idea is furthermore repudiated by the fact that Edison's Kinetograph camera was by this time complete.

As a result of the bankruptcy of a company in which he had an interest, Friese-Greene found himself in prison in 1891. And

thereafter he began to squander his energies, worked on stereoscopic film, on stage effects, went to the Ministry of War with
schemes for photographing manoeuvres from a balloon, devised
theories about colour film, invented a method for reproducing
pictures which was used by the firm of Wills in Bristol, to make
the little pictorial cards included in packets of cigarettes for
advertising purposes (a practice that still survives, though the
Friese-Greene process was soon abandoned). He was a harried,
hunted man. Certainly he was not one of the great inventors of
his century. Rather, he was full of inspirations – he took out
seventy-eight British patents between 1889 and 1921, yet not
one became the basis for an industry. For all that, it is distress-
ing to learn that this man died at a congress of cinema people
in the midst of a stammering, high-flown speech he attempted
to deliver – to an audience in which no one recognised the old
man. A shilling and ten pence were found in his pockets. It was
a brilliant stroke on the part of his biographer to add that this
sum was the price of a seat in the cinema.[6]

The work of the third of this group has not yet been properly
evaluated. Jean Aimé Le Roy (born 1854), an American despite
his name, issued a programme on February 22, 1895, announc-
ing a Cinématographe. This was one week before Lumière's
first closed performance; at the time Lumière had not yet used
this name. Le Roy, a photographer, had begun in 1876 to im-
prove on Heyl's Phenakisticope. He photographed *Children's
Waltz* in two hundred phase pictures, and projected the trans-

parent positive plates. It appears that he was not so much a creative inventor as a good organiser. In 1893 he obtained film from Donisthorpe in England; then he bought Edison films; then he secured the collaboration of Eugène Lauste, a Frenchman who had worked under Dickson in Edison's laboratory. He combined the work of others with his own. In partnership with Lauste he founded the Cinematograph Novelty Company on February 5, 1894. Only twenty days later he gave a showing of continuous pictures in the business offices of the optical firm of Riley Brothers in New York. In January 1895 he founded a new Cinematograph company and gave more performances. He continued doing so for two years more; some of these were probably the first cinematograph performances for a *paying* public. Then the trail of this first entrepreneur vanishes.[7]

These are far from all who pioneered in this field. The Latham family must be mentioned – simply for the sake of the date. Two brothers, Grey and Otway Latham, apothecary salesmen, founded the Kinetoscope Exhibition Company. It was a failure. Their father, Major Woodville Latham, came to their assistance, and in December 1894 they founded the Lambda Company (one of them must have had some classical education; the Greek *L* stood for Latham). At this point the record becomes vague. Apparently they put on genuine cinematographic shows on Frankford Street in New York. On May 20 they opened on Broadway, but received very poor notices – the more discouraging for a time in which everything new was hailed enthusiastically.

Fifty others could be named. Or we might mention some of the innumerable devices and types of apparatus. Among the most striking names for the new attraction were: Getthemoney-graph (probably the best name of the lot, since it is admirably frank about its purpose), Chronophotographoscope, Counter-fivoscope, Phantasmagoria, Klondikoscope, Vileocigraphi-scope.

There was no end to them. And none can be taken as the crucial one by the historian of the film. All of them were merely also-rans.

One pair of brothers, however, whose cause has been espous-ed for decades by patriotic German cinema historians, must be assigned their proper place.[8]

Max and Emil Skladanowsky were showmen. Along with their father, they had been producing 'dissolving views' for years. Max (1863–1939) was the technical-minded brother. He early became interested in making series photographs with Eastman Kodak celluloid film, and seeking a way to exploit these commercially, hit on the idea of projecting them. Be-tween 1892 and 1895 he developed the Bioscope. By all tokens it was an independently invented device.

On November 1, 1895, the brothers set up their Bioscope in the Berlin Wintergarten to project the intermittent photographs which they had taken on Eastman film rolls. They had reached a speed of eight frames per second; by repeated copying they had arrived at rough positive frames, which they cut up, pasted together into two ribbons each of twenty pictures apiece (each frame 3 by 4 cm.), perforated with metal eyelets, and threw on a screen from a double projector. Their actual patent (N° 88,599) describes a crude worm-gear mechanism (as Skladanowsky proudly notes: 'Which was manufactured, on the basis of my drawings, for 150,25 marks in 258 hours of labour... by the Berlin firm of Mehre and Schäfer from high-quality special steel...'). This mechanism guided the intermittent movement of the film strip

The performances in the Wintergarten Variety Show were billed as, 'The Bioscope, the most interesting and amusing invention of modern times', which was put on at the end of the Variety Programme as a 'parting shot'. The press regarded the offering as a further development of the Kinetoscope,[9] or of Anschütz' Tachyscope,[10] and the majority of the newspapers were impressed but not especially enthusiastic.[11] The Bioscope programme showed two children doing a peasant dance, two gymnasts working on the horizontal bar, a kangaroo boxing match, a juggler, a group of dancers, a boxing match, and a family doing gymnastics.[12]

November 1, 1895, is important because Skladanowsky put on a public performance with film strips he himself had photographed, and with a projector he himself had built. Those who call him the 'inventor of the cinema' rest their case on this fact; for although the Lumières had given private showings seven months before Skladanowsky, they did not exhibit to a paying public until two months after. The thesis, however, lays too much stress upon a triviality.[13] G. M. Coissac is of course wrong when he decries the Bioscope as a fable of the Nazis.[14] But in fact the Bioscope, as a double projector, was to have no future. None of its parts were adopted in new devices, and while further performances of it were given in Germany, Holland and Scandinavia, it was no longer in use after 1896. Moreover, the Skladanowskys with their circular films could offer only series pictures, not the continuous pictures which represent real cinema. Le Prince had long ago progressed beyond these endless strips in which the last movement merged into the first. The misfortune of the Skladanowskys was their milieu; they were born into it and never rose above it.[15]

The men who showed the first real films in our sense of documentary and story cinema, who suddenly came forth with devices mature enough to create an industry, and who established the first cinema theatres, were the Frenchmen Auguste and Louis Lumière.

Louis Jean Lumière (1864–1948) was always scrupulous about sharing the credit for any of his inventions with his elder brother, Auguste Marie Louis Nicolas (1862–1954). Today we know that the ideas which resulted in cinematography sprang chiefly from the mind of the younger brother.[16] Their father, Antoine, was an active photographer, and the brothers grew up in the profession. Louis, a lover of the fine arts, wavered as to whether he should devote himself to art or science – but not for long. When he espoused cinematography, after thoroughly studying the work of Anschütz, Reynaud and Edison, he did so as an industrialist. The Lumières owned a factory in Lyons where all kinds of photographic products were made. Although the brothers worked for nearly half a year on preliminary devices, the actual invention took place as we like to think of inventions being made: in a flash of inspiration. '*Mon frère, en une nuit, avait inventé le cinématographe*' – a night, moreover, during which he was suffering from feverish dreams and migraine, Auguste tells us.[17]

On February 13, 1895, this invention of a single night – camera and projector contained in a single apparatus – was patented and assigned Number 245,932.[18] Its special characteristic was expressed in its name: *Kinétoscope de (en) projection*. But this was soon changed (in spite of many legal suits) to Cinématographe. The name has remained attached to the device to this day. Other elements have also remained. Lumière followed the practice invented by Edison of perforating his film strips. His first films, however, had single-hole perforations. His most important contribution was an eccentrically driven claw drive for moving the film strip.

On March 22, 1895, at the rue de Rennes 44 in Paris the Lumières presented their first film to the Société d'Encouragement pour l'Industrie Nationale. Its title was *La Sortie des Ouvriers de l'Usine Lumière* ('Workers leaving the Lumière Factory').[19]

Further performances, with an enlarged programme of eight picture strips, were given on June 10, 1895, at the congress of the Sociétés Photographiques de France in Lyons, in the great hall of the Palais de la Bourse; then on June 12, on July 11, on November 10 in Brussels, on November 16 at the Sorbonne in Paris. These were all put on for an audience of invited specialists. On December 28, 1895, however, the first public performance took place – in the Salon Indien of the Grand Café, Boulevard des Capucines 14 in Paris.[20] The brothers had more pressing affairs than to be present at these shows. Père Antoine Lumière was glad to preside over the ceremonies. The admission was a franc. The first day brought in thirty-five francs; within a short time the takings increased to 300 francs per day. Since the newspapers had received no advertisements, they were rather reticent about reporting the shows during the first few days, but later they carried enthusiastic notices.

The most striking numbers on the first programmes[21] were *L'Arrivée d'un train en gare* and *L'Arroseur arrosé.*[22] In the first the train appeared in the distance and rolled to a close-up – a thrill for the spectator, who even today cannot help drawing back when the same trick is pulled and the train seems to be hurtling directly at him. The second was the first example of cinema farce: a boy pinches a gardener's hose, the gardener examines the nozzle, receives a stream of water in his face, and spanks the boy. This, too, is a subject that still fetches a laugh.

In 1897 the Lumières' first big catalogue appeared, printed by Decléris et Fils in Lyons. It listed 358 different strips, up to seventeen metres in length, under the following headings: Vues générales, Vues comiques, France, Algérie, Tunisie, Allemagne, Angleterre, Espagne, Autriche-Hongrie, Russie, Suisse, Amérique du Nord.

The titles alone suggest the range and variety. The film on Germany contained pictures of the Panoptikum in Friedrich-strasse and of Potsdamer Platz in Berlin. Three strips covered the 'Unveiling of the Monument to William I': 1. Before the Unveiling; 2. The Unveiling; 3. Parade of the Hussars before William II; then William II and Nicholas II on Horseback; finally pictures of Cologne, Dresden, Frankfurt am Main, Hamburg, Munich, Stuttgart. Numbers 218 to 245 all dealt with Germany. Oddly enough, Spain provided the highest number of strips on military matters – nine.

This first catalogue thus included what we today would call brief story films, documentary films, cultural films, and even trick films, such as *Démolition d'un mur I–II* (in which a wall is torn down and then, the film being turned backward, puts itself together again).

By 1898 six more catalogues had appeared, with a total of one thousand films – amazing productivity *before* the creation of a cinema industry. The lists contained the first historical films: a *Faust* in two parts, a *Life and Passion of Jesus Christ*, and films on Nero and Napoleon. The Catalogue général of 1901 listed 1299 titles.

The films produced before 1897 had already made the cine-matographic theatre a necessity. It was only natural that the great showmen were the first to see the possibilities of this medium. Georges Méliès of the Théâtre Houdin offered 10,000 francs for the rights to the Lumières' process; Thomas, Director of the Musée Grévin, 20,000; Lallemand, Director of the Folies Bergères, 50,000. The Lumières declined these offers. They went on making films because they regarded each new strip as a scientific problem. But they also opened cinemas or gave licences to friends and associates. Thus, in the first months of 1896 alone, cinematograph theatres were opened in Lyons on January 25; London on February 17; Bordeaux on February 18, Brussels on February 29; Berlin on April 30; New York on June 18.

In April 1896 the cinematograph was shown in Vienna to Emperor Franz Josef; on June 12 to the Queen of Spain; on June 25 to the King of Serbia; on July 7 and 25 to the Tsar and Tsarina – all important events in an age when royalty's smile was the supreme endorsement.

Within France, the Lumières were regarded as genuine inventors. And so they were. Tinkerers, they earned glory – for invention in those days was still tinkering. They came even closer than Edison to our present-day concept of laboratory inventing; but they did not establish a laboratory with associates working toward a particular goal. Rather, they had a laboratory already, and out of it sprang the most surprising inventions, from the cinematograph to a prosthetic hand for the wounded of World War I.

The Lumières, before the turn of the century, were faced with the alternatives of remaining pure inventors or going into the field of manufacturing, with all the tempting profits that entailed. They made a clear choice. When their devices called for new production methods, for entering into alien realms, they went along only for a time, then hastily returned to their laboratories. But during those years the cinema came into being, because a cinema industry arose.[23]

Notes to the text

1 First patent as early as November 2, 1886: U.S.P. N° 376,247.
2 On the importance of this invention, see page 1.
3 The quality of all these experiments can only be guessed at today. Eyewitness accounts are rather late and inexact. Patent applications never give a clear technical exposition. Some of the apparatuses can no longer be found. There is no doubt that Le Prince made a number of devices; but the question of how far his experiments succeeded cannot be entirely decided. Neither his film strips nor the devices subsequently found in Leeds afford complete clarity.
4 1855–1921. R. Allister: *Friese-Greene* (London, 1948) must be read with caution. An obituary more than a biography, a laudatory funeral oration rather than an attempt at clarification; but full of good material. For a scholarly and penetrating revaluation of Friese-Greene's work see Brian Coe's articles in the March and April issues of *The Photographic Journal*, 1962.
5 The letter is said to have contained precise drawings. Edison later declared that he had never received it. This is a question an industrious researcher would find worth looking into.

6　Allister: *Friese-Greene*, p. 180. But in June 1952, at the Berlin film festival, the British showed a story film, *The Magic Box*, dedicated to Friese-Greene.

7　According to Sadoul, *Histoire*, vol. I, p. 174, he was still heard of in 1937. In Reinert's *Filmlexikon*, an otherwise excellent pioneering book, he is not mentioned at all. Neither Rotha in the 755 pages of his *The Film Till Now*, nor Jacobs in *The Rise of the American Film*, mention his name.

8　Taking diametrically opposite views on this question are C. Niessen: *Der 'Film', eine unabhängige deutsche Erfindung* (1934) and Forch: *Der Kinematograph und das sich bewegende Bild* (Leipzig, 1913). An uncritical appreciation in H. Hopwood: *Living Pictures* (London, 1899, p. 107). In addition, two hectographed essays by Max Skladanowsky: *Es war einmal ein Filmatelier in Pankow* (c. 1936) and *Der Jubilar des Films, Max Skladanowsky, 75 Jahre alt* (1938).

9　*Volkszeitung*, Berlin, November 4, 1895. Max Skladanowsky later always included with his programmes a hectographed list of fourteen press notices.

10　*Berliner Zeitung*, November 5, 1895.

11　The correspondent of the *Staatsbürger-Zeitung*, Berlin, November 5, 1895, seems to have shown the greatest admiration: 'The finale of the performance leaps across the little stage of the Bioscope. The ingenious technician here employs amusing instantaneous photograms (sic!) and shows them in enlarged form, not rigidly, but alive. The devil only knows how he does it.'

12 American encyclopedias to this day wrongly designate as the 'very first public film performance' the showing with Edison's Vitascope in Koster and Bial's Variety Show in New York on April 20, 1896. This is inaccurate in respect both to the work of the Skladanowskys and that of the Lumières.

13 All sorts of subsequent falsifications contributed to the overestimation. When the Skladanowskys were rediscovered in the Twenties, their work was judged from a mélange of genuine 1895 photographs with documentary moving pictures of 1896–1897, recopied on standard modern film and viewed with a modern projector, not a Bioscope. Hence such inaccurate phrases as the one on the Wintergarten plaque; see the legend on page 11. Max Skladanowsky, in a conversation with me in 1938, admitted the recopying, but refused to regard it as a falsification. Incidentally, *all* cinema 'incunabula' shown today should be viewed with the greatest caution; recopied and reproduced by modern projectors, they reveal their original character much as would a 1904 Ford car sent to a rally equipped with a 1964 Mercury motor.

14 In *Le Cinéma*, edited by H. Fescourt (Paris, 1932), p. 61. He constantly refers to the brothers 'Kladanowski', lists them among 'pseudo-inventors', and argues that even the German technicians, until the Nazis exhumed the Bioscope,

'n'ont jamais connu les traveaux des frères Kladanowski'. This is false.

15 The Englishman Birt Acres occupies a position similar to that of the Skladanowskys. His apparatus (patent N° 10,474) was demonstrated to the Royal Photographic Society on January 14, 1896, and included the projection of film strips of the Derby of 1895 and the opening of the Kiel Canal by the German Emperor.

16 On their cinematographic work, see Traub: *Als man anfing zu filmen;* on the Lumières' life, personality and inventions in general, see M. Bessy and L. Duca: *Louis Lumière* (1948) and H. Kubnik: *Les frères Lumière* (1938).

17 Louis Lumière, in conversation with me in 1938, personally attested to this fact. It is not widely known – which must be the only reason that essayists so far have overlooked the chance to point up this symbolic birth of the dream-factory from a dream. Let us hope they now make up for the omission.

18 For exact description of the cinematographic principles of the first Lumière devices, see Bessy and Duca, op. cit., pp. 31 to 39.

19 It is pointless to try to establish 'the world's first film'. The first strip of continuous pictures might be called that. Certainly the first such strip that was *projected* deserves the title. The important fact is this: With the presentation of March 22, 1895, the time of experiment was over and the 'cinema' began to affect the world.

20 This café has disappeared. But the second Lumière cinema in Paris, Number 6 Boulevard St Denis, seems to have existed for a long time. Since it was opened towards the end of 1896, it probably deserves to be called the oldest cinema in the world.

21 The chronology is dubious. The Lumières' first catalogue was arranged alphabetically within subject groups. Nor is it possible to determine with any certainty which strips were produced by the Lumières personally; from 1896 on the Lumière factory employed outside cameramen. See Bessy and Duca, op. cit., p. 70.

22 Title of the 1896 version. The first version was called *Le jardinier* or *Le jardinier et le petit espiègle*. The first cinema poster was made for this film – by M. Auzolle; the contemporary poster by H. Brispot served as an announcement of the entire show.

23 Details of the chemical, physical and optical improvements, which would be interesting only to the technical expert, have been omitted from this book. Concerning these, see the works of Rudolph Thun and G. Michel Coissac. For a survey, Lo Duca: *Technique de Cinéma*. Details on the development of various types of apparatus in all countries, also titles and numbers of the critical patents, have been assembled by Jean Vivié: *Traite général de technique du cinéma*, Vol. I: *Historique et développement de la technique cinématographique*. The statements by the Soviet historian, E. M. Goldowski, in *Thirty Years of Soviet Film*

Technique, must be examined with a highly critical eye. He uses sparse and inexact data on a number of nineteenth-century inventions in the fields of electrical technology and physics (unrealized or subsequently impracticable early versions of batteries, arc-lights, transformers, electric lights, reflectors) to come to the conclusion: 'There can be no doubt that the idea of cinematography itself was based upon a number of extremely ingenious discoveries and inventions by Russian scholars.' Or: 'It [the silent film] became possible only due to the brilliant discoveries of our fellow-countrymen during the nineteenth century.' This sentence, by the way, contains the only tacit admission of the fact that the actual inventions were made by non-Russians. The name Lumière is not mentioned in the historical section of the Russian's book.

TO THE ASTOUNDING BIOSCOPE

The word Bioscope recalls more than any other term the early days of projection. Less precise than the names of the scientific toys, Phenakisticope, Zoetrope or Praxinoscope, it was applied both to the experimental projectors of men like Dubosq and Foucauld who combined glass plates with the Phenakisticope, and to the more developed apparatus of Demeny, Skladanowsky, Birt Acres and Paul. Even when cinematography had been commercialized Charles Urban called his projector the Bioscope and for many an early picture-goer that magic word summed up the whole entertainment. (187)

Many pioneers are claimed as the 'true inventors' of the cinema. Varley, Friese-Greene, Edison, Dickson, Le Roy, Robert Paul, Wordsworth Donisthorpe, Le Prince, Latham, Birt Acres, Demeny, the Lumières and Skladanowsky by no means complete the list of names. Louis Aimé Augustin Le Prince had been the manager of a famous military panorama in New York, Washington and Chicago before turning his attention to cinematography. In 1888 in his Leeds workshop he invented a projector camera with which he would probably have succeeded in exhibiting films to large audiences if he had not mysteriously disappeared in 1890. Right, portions of film strips taken by Le Prince in October 1888 showing traffic on Leeds bridge and a scene on the lawn of his house in Leeds. The date of the latter is proved by the fact that his mother-in-law, who appears in the picture, died on October 24th 1888. (188–191)

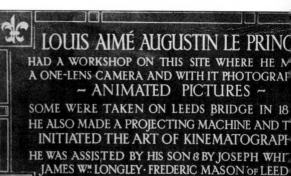

LOUIS AIMÉ AUGUSTIN LE PRINC[E]
HAD A WORKSHOP ON THIS SITE WHERE HE M[ADE]
A ONE-LENS CAMERA AND WITH IT PHOTOGRA[PHED]
~ ANIMATED PICTURES ~
SOME WERE TAKEN ON LEEDS BRIDGE IN 18[88]
HE ALSO MADE A PROJECTING MACHINE AND T[HUS]
INITIATED THE ART OF KINEMATOGRAP[HY]
HE WAS ASSISTED BY HIS SON & BY JOSEPH WHIT[LEY]
JAMES W. LONGLEY · FREDERIC MASON of LEED[S]
This tablet was placed here by public subscription.

Le Prince's first camera projector, constructed in 1887, had sixteen lenses. He improved on this and produced a single-lens camera projector (opposite) in 1888. This was the first single-lens camera with which cinematography pictures were taken at the rate of 20 per second. With it, using perforated film, Le Prince took the strips shown on the previous page. Below, spools used by Le Prince in 1888. (192–194)

W. Friese-Greene (below), whose high reputation as a motion picture pioneer has recently been subjected to close scrutiny, patented a camera and projector system in 1893, but there is no evidence of a satisfactory projection. The camera, although similar in structure to those which achieved complete success in 1895, does not appear to have been capable of taking pictures at sufficient speed to produce a convincing effect of movement. Friese-Greene owed much to J. A. R. Rudge upon whose Phantascope and Biophantascope lanterns his first experiments were based. (195, 196)

TO PERPETUATE THE NAME AND MEMORY OF
JOHN ARTHUR ROEBUCK RUDGE
WHO LIVED FOR MANY YEARS IN THE ADJOINING HOUSE AND AFTER NUMEROUS EXPERIMENTS CONDUCTED IN THE BASEMENT WAS THE FIRST ENGLISHMAN TO PRODUCE MOVING PICTURES BY MEANS OF PHOTOGRAPHS MOUNTED ON A REVOLVING DRUM
AND ALSO OF HIS FRIEND
WILLIAM FRIESE-GREENE
WHO HAD HIS STUDIO AT N°9 THE CORRIDOR NEARBY. THE INVENTOR OF COMMERCIAL KINEMATOGRAPHY. BEING THE FIRST MAN TO APPLY CELLULOID RIBBON FOR THIS PURPOSE.
KINEMATOGRAPHY CAN THUS BE ATTRIBUTED TO THE LABOURS OF THESE TWO CITIZENS OF BATH WHERE THIS WONDERFUL INVENTION UNDOUBTEDLY RECEIVED ITS BIRTH.

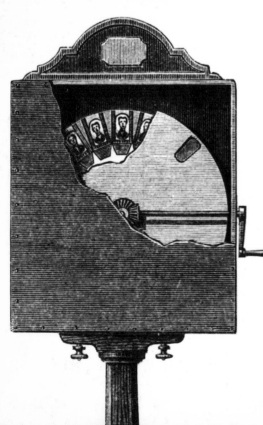

orges Demeny worked for a number of **rs** with Professor Marey. In 1892 he patent**ed** his Phonoscope for taking and reproducing **al** and other movements. The camera em**ployed** two counter-rotating discs, one a slotted **shutter** behind the lens, the other situated behind **the** shutter and carrying a sensitive emulsion. **The** negatives were printed as positives and **used** in a similar apparatus for viewing or **projection.** Demeny calculated that through **photographs** of speech the deaf could learn to **speak;** he therefore specialized in close-ups of **himself** uttering such simple phrases as 'Vive la **France'** or 'Je vous aime'. In 1895 Demeny be**came** associated with Léon Gaumont and rebap**tized** his apparatus 'Bioscope'. The 60-mm. film **strip** on the right was taken in 1896. (197–200)

ueen's Hall, at 7.30 and 9 o'clock.

* * *

The Kineopticon,

INVENTED AND PATENTED BY

BIRT ACRES, ESQ., F.R.Met.S., F.R.P.S.

Introduced by MR. T. C. HAYWARD.

*

A Selection will be shown from the following List of Subjects:—

1. SEA WAVES AT DOVER.
   The waves roll up in a most realistic manner, breaking against the Admiralty Pier, each wave as it breaks throwing up a great cloud of spray.

2. GOLFING EXTRAORDINARY—5 GENTLEMEN.
   This is a Golf Scene, in which one gentleman in attempting to strike the ball misses and falls headlong, much to the amusement of the bystanders.

3. TOM MERRY, "LIGHTNING CARTOONIST," SKETCHING GLADSTONE.

4. TOM MERRY, "LIGHTNING CARTOONIST," SKETCHING SALISBURY.
   In these two pictures Mr. Tom Merry, the Lightning Cartoonist, is seen busy at work upon portraits of Mr. Gladstone and Lord Salisbury.

5. BOXING MATCH OR GLOVE CONTEST.
   Having an interval introduced, during which the combatants sit down for a brief rest, and are vigorously fanned by two attendants, concluding in the last round with one of the boxers being floored.

6. HIGHGATE TUNNEL.
   A goods train issues from the tunnel and passes through Highgate Station; a gentleman, waiting for his train, strolls up and down the platform and watches the passing trucks.

7. HENLEY REGATTA.
   This year's picture, showing the whole surface of the river crowded with boats, &c.

ARREST OF A PICKPOCKET,

which the man is pursued by a constable, runs right across the
ture, they struggle together and the policeman's helmet is knocked
then the pickpocket, by slipping out of his jacket, manages to
ape, but runs full tilt into the arms of a sailor, with whose
istance he is finally secured, handcuffed, and marched off to justice.

DWAY—NEW YORK.

busy scene at Broadway, with carriages, trams, carts, and
lestrians moving about.

CE AND PRINCESS OF WALES AT CARDIFF, JUNE 27TH.

view of the Prince and Princess of Wales, the Princesses Victoria
d Maud, and their suite, on the occasion of their visit to the
rdiff Exhibition, in which portrait pictures of the Royal group are
:hfully reproduced.

oove subjects are the identical pictures exhibited before H.R.H.
:e of Wales and the Royal Wedding Guests, at Marlborough
a Tuesday, July 21st, 1896. At the close of the Entertainment,
omplimented Mr. Acres on the successful exhibit, and honoured
special permission to photograph the Royal Wedding on the
day.

✴✴✴

omenade Concert

In the QUEEN'S HALL, at 8 o'clock.

✷✷

ES IRON WORKS' MILITARY BAND

(By kind permission of A. F. HILLS, Esq.),

: MR. JOHN H. WILLIAMS, Bandmaster Thames Iron Works' Military
Band, and 2nd Kent Volunteer Artillery.

:alists : MISS ANNIE SWALLOW, MR. ARTHUR WESTON,
MR. FRED DANIELS, Coster Comedian.

:H—"Argandab"	*T. Thompson.*
—"The Carnival"—	*Molloy.*
MR. ARTHUR WESTON.	
.TURE—"La Ruche D'or"	*E. Brepsant.*

Birt Acres was the first Englishman successfully to produce and publicly show
animated pictures. He patented his apparatus in May 1895 and after several private demonstrations he projected a number of films to the Royal Photographic
Society on January 14th 1896. The name
he eventually gave to his machine was
'Kineopticon'. *The Sea Waves at Dover*,
the first item on the Queen's Hall programme, was taken by Acres with a
camera constructed by R. W. Paul. (201,
202)

inematograph camera for 35-mm. film (left) later to become
standard width, patented by Birt Acres in May, 1895. Above,
t Acres with his camera filming the Derby which was among
items projected to the Royal Photographic Society on Janu-
14th 1896. (203–205)

In November 1895 Max and Emil Skladanowsky projected a number of variety acts by means of their Bioscope, a double projector, in the Berlin Wintergarten. This home-made apparatus owed nothing to other pioneers and made use of perforated celluloid to secure intermittent movement. Right, film strips taken by Max Skladanowsky in 1896, *Traffic in the Alexanderplatz* and *The Changing of the Guard, Unter den Linden.* (206–209)

themes of early film strips frequently derived from vaudeville. One of
most popular numbers on the variety stage of the nineties was the Serpen-
Dance and among those who demonstrated it two of the best known dan-
were Mlle Ançion, left, filmed by Max Skladanowsky in 1896, and Anna-
le the Dancer (Annabelle Whitford Moore), above, photographed for Edi-
's Kinetoscope. This film was included in the programme given at Koster
Bial's Music Hall, New York, on April 23rd 1896 on the occasion of the
projection of Edison's Kinetoscope films by means of Thomas Armat's
ascope. (210, 211)

True cinematographic films were first exhibited to a *paying* public
the brothers Louis and Auguste Lumière, right, on December 28th 189
the Grand Café, Boulevard des Capucins, Paris. The price of admiss
was one franc. Above, Louis Lumière filming out of doors; top right,
Lumière 'cinématographe' a combined ciné camera, printer and proje
constructed by the Jules Carpentier manufacturing firm. The apparatus u

mm. perforated film and a claw movement. The projectors of the
commercial cinema differed from the Lumière machine in that they
achieved intermittent movement by means of the Maltese Cross, the ad-
vantages of which were recognized by the German pioneer Oskar Messter.
The cross, which is mounted on the same shaft as a film sprocket, serves
to move the sprocket round by the space of one picture at a time. (212–214)

The first Lumière film was *La Sortie des Ouvriers de l'Usine Lumière à Lyon.* (215)

mière's first public film show included *Le Repas de Bébé*, a
~~u~~ure of Auguste and Mme Lumière and their infant daughter
~~b~~reakfast, *Partie d'Ecarte* and *L'Arrivée d'un Train en Gare*.
~~thi~~s film included the thrilling spectacle of a train rushing to-
~~war~~ds the audience, and was reminiscent of the Phantasmagoria
~~effe~~cts which had been exhibited earlier in the century only a
~~few~~ yards distant from the Grand Café. (216–218)

EMPIRE THEATRE.

CINÉMATOGRAPHE,

LUMIERE'S.

THE CINÉMATOGRAPHE,

hich the Directors of the Empire have pleasure in submitting
you, needs little introduction. It is a scientific con-
ivance which accomplishes nothing less marvellous than the
esentation before an Empire audience of accurate records,
stinct with life and actuality, of real living moving scenes.
he development of instantaneous photography has rendered
is marvellous result possible. By the employment of a highly
gelatine band, act ted by most ingenious mechanism,
series of instantaneous snapshot photographs of a living
ene are taken with such rapidity that all the varying suc-
ssive phases of the movement of a crowd, the bustle of a
ilway station, the actions of a man at work, even the restless
otion of the sea, the curl of the breakers, and the dashing of
e waves in spray upon the rocks, are faithfully recorded for
l time. These photographs are taken at the rate of over 900
er minute. When they a e passed once more through the
inématographe and projected by means of a powerful electric
ght upon the screen, the succession of images following one
nother in the same order and with the same rapidity with
hich they were taken, the effect is to reconstitute the scenes
hich they record with the most marvellous fidelity and
aturalness. The interval during which one picture is sub-
tituted for a succeeding one is so infinitesimal, that, the retina
the eye preserving one image until the next one takes its
lace, an effect of absolute continuity and perfect illusion
f life is obtained.

The following Pictures will be s

Dinner Hour at the Factory Ga
Lumiere at Lyons.

Tea Time.

The Blacksmith at Work.

A Game at Écarté.

The Arrival of the Paris Expres

Children at Play.

A Practical Joke on the Garden

Trewey's Serpentine Ribbon.

Place des Cordeliers (Lyons).

Bathing in the Mediterranean.

Under the Sole Management of Monsieur

The first slapstick comedy of the cinema was *L'Arroseur arr*
another of the films shown in Lumière's first programme. It
featured in the exhibition of the Lumière Cinématographe at
Empire Theatre London in 1896 and is the subject of the pos
right. (219–221)

NÉMATOGRAPHE LUMIÉR

According to record, the first public
Show of Lumiere's Cinématographe, took
place at the Regent St Polytechnic.
1896. By Prof. Trewey.

But he also gave performances at
the Empire Theatre, Leicester Squar
in the same year.; the first, a privat
Show in the Stalls foyer
The Apparatus was eventually presented
to the Kensington Museum by Mr Da

The fame of the Cinématographe quickly spread. Within a
few weeks the Lumière films were playing to more than two
thousand people a day. The Cinématographe was shown in
London at the Polytechnic institution in March 1896 and began
its successful run at the Empire Theatre Leicester Square soon
afterwards under the management of F. Trewey, former shadow
showman and magician and, like Athanasius Kircher, trained as
a Jesuit priest. In the same year, 1896, the Cinématographe was
exhibited in all the chief cities of Europe; it was first shown in
New York in June 1896 at Keith's 14th Street Theatre. (222, 223)

Panel 1 (top left)

Aux heures et aux demies:
Le matin de 10 à 11 h. 1/2; l'après-midi de 2 h. à 6 h. 1/2
Le soir de 8 h. à 11 h.

LE CINÉMATOGRAPHE
LUMIÈRE
GRAND CAFÉ
14, Boulevard des Capucines, 14
PARIS

Cet appareil, inventé par MM. Auguste et Louis Lumière, permet de recueillir, par des séries d'épreuves instantanées, tous les mouvements qui, pendant un temps donné, se sont succédé devant l'objectif, et de reproduire ensuite ces mouvements en projetant, grandeur naturelle, devant une salle entière leurs images sur un écran.

SUJETS ACTUELS

1 Sortie de l'usine LUMIÈRE à Lyon.	6 Maréchal-Ferrant
2 Querelle de bébés	7 Partie d'écarté.
3 Bassin des Tuileries.	8 Mauvaises herbes.
4 Le train.	9 Le mur
5 Le régiment.	10 La mer.

La Direction se réserve le droit, en cas de force majeure, de remplacer un des Tableaux porté au programme par un autre.

LE CINÉMATOGRAPHE PEUT FONCTIONNER DANS LES SALONS.

Spécimen de l'un des premiers programmes de séance cinématographique.

Panel 2 (top right)

Second Visit of this, the finest Organization Travelling.

The success of this Company in Northampton 12 months ago will be remembered.

Temperance Hall, Northampton.
FOR TEN DAYS ONLY.
Commencing Christmas Day, December 25th, 1896.
Nightly at 7-45. Doors open 7-15.
PRICES.—Reserved Seats, 2/0; Second Class, 1/-; Third Class, 6d.
Juveniles half-price. Carriages at 10-30.
DAY PERFORMANCES—Christmas Day; Boxing Day; Monday, Dec. 28th; and Saturday, Jan. 2nd, at 3 p.m. Doors open at 2-30.

MR. GUSTAVE ROSELLE'S ROYAL

COURT CHOIR

New Combination of
LADY MINSTRELS and ORCHESTRA.
The finest Orchestral Band travelling.
13 Members in Costume. English, Irish, Scotch, and Welsh Vocalists. Players on all kinds of Foreign Instruments.
BEAUTIFUL PICTURES! LAUGHABLE SKETCHES!
The PICTORIAL TOURS comprise the following "Bonnie Scotland," "Round the World," "London to India," and "Holland, Belgium, and the Rhine."

And the Latest Society Sensation, the greatest Psychological Bewilderment on Earth,

MISS NELLIE ROSELLE
Scientific Clairvoyant, in her Mysterious DREAM VISIONS.
This wonderful lady gives information of missing friends, stolen and lost property, advice on business and marriage, in fact, answers any question submitted to her.

The PHOTO-ELECTRIC SENSATION of the AGE,

THE SCENIMATOGRAPHE
LIVING MOVING PICTURES.
This wonderful instrument produces as it were accurate records of Real, Living, Moving Scenes of Ever-day Life, all the Varying, Successive Movements of a Crowd, the bustle of a Railway Station with Passing Trains, the River Thames with its Steamers passing to and fro, Busy London Thoroughfares with Continual Streams of Traffic, every movement of which is faithfully recorded

ENTIRE CHANGE OF PROGRAMME EVERY EVENING.

SACRED CONCERTS on Sundays, Dec. 27th, and Jan. 3rd, at 8-15, by the Royal Court Choir and Orchestra. Admission by Collection. Best Seats Silver.

HOLORAN & Co., Printers, Retford.

Panel 3 (bottom left)

To-Night! To-Night!

CALDER'S FAMOUS
CINEMATOGRAPH
AND
Popular Concert.

Don't miss seeing the Grand NEW PICTURES of
THE DREYFUS COURT MARTIAL.
The Prince of Wales in Edinburgh.
Sir Redvers Buller Embarking for Transvaal.
Scenes at the Highland Brigade Camp.
The Invercharron Gathering.
The Grand Fire Dance.
Barnum & Bailey's Procession.
The Mysterious Astrologer's Dream.
Spendid Train Scenes.
Grand Coloured Dances.
Comicalities and Burlesque Scenes, &c., &c.
Pictures of absorbing interest and Astounding Transformations.

SPLENDID · CONCERT
By First-Class Artistes.

DOORS OPEN AT 7.30. CONCERT AT 8 P.M.
Popular Prices—See Bills.

A BRIGHT, UP-TO-DATE, SPARKLING ENTERTAINMENT.

Panel 4 (bottom right)

NEXT WEEK!!
AT
THE EMPIRE.
Once Again at Great Expense,
THE ORIGINAL ..
.. UNSURPASSED ..
.. UNEQUALLED
. LUMIERE .
CINEMATOGRAPHE

From the Empire, London,
Under the Direction of M. TREWEY.

A Series of Brilliant and Interesting Scenes absolutely true to life in
PRECISION, PROPORTION AND MOTION.

Towerskay in Moscow.	Soldiers' Parade in Madrid.
Children—Cat and Dog.	Concorde Bridge, Paris.
The Disappointed Artist.	Lancers in Stuttgart.
Burmese Dance at the Crystal Palace.	Artillery in Barcelona.
Hamburg Bridge, Germany.	Fire Brigade Call, London.
	Charge of Cavalry in France.

AND
A Remarkable Picture—"TOBOGGANING IN SWITZERLAND."

You would have to expend a large amount of money and time to obtain a view of the Scenes of the above Programme in their Geographical situation, but by the aid of this wonderful instrument in conjunction with Motor Photography, they are brought before you exact in form and motion for the money and time a visit to the Empire entails.

Tudor Printing Works, Cardiff. 14916

Cinématographe advertisements from the years 1896 and 1897. The motion picture at this date was usually but one of many items in a music hall programme. (224–227)

WINDSOR CASTLE.

Tuesday, 23rd November, 1897.

By Command of Her Most Gracious Majesty the Queen.

PROGRAMME.

PART I.

Overture ... ... "Le Cid" ... ... *J. Massenet.*

CINEMATOGRAPHE PICTURES.	PROGRAMME OF MUSIC.
1. The Bois de Boulogne.	1. Pas de Cinq, from "Monte Cristo" Ballet, *L. Wenzel.*
2. The Czar of Russia in Paris.	2. Marche du Couronnement ... *Preisgekrönt.*
3. Spanish Dancers in Castille.	3. Danse Espagnole, from "Dolly" Ballet, *L. Wenzel.*
4. A Charge of French Cavalry.	4. Infanterie Cavalerie Charge ... *C. Millöker.*
5. Blacksmiths at Work.	5.⎫ Les Volontaires Marche ... *O. Métra.*
6. Hussars passing through Dublin,	6.⎭
7. Carnival at Nice.	7. Le Petit Bleu Valse ... ... *L. Wenzel.*

PART II.

"Philemon et Baucis" ... ... *Ch. Gounod.*

8. A Scene in Parliament Street.	8.⎫ Loin du Bal ... ... *E. Gillet.*
9. The Disputed Fare.	9.⎭
10. A Soudanese Swimming Bath.	10.⎫ Valse, from "By the Sea" Ballet... *L.Wenzel.*
11. A Joke on the Gardener.	11.⎭
12. Serpentine and Butterfly Dances.	12. Valse, from "Versailles" Ballet ... *L. Wenzel.*
13. The Naval Review.	13. A life on the Ocean, Nautical Selection, *E. Binding.*

PART III.

Monsieur Taffary's Calculating and Performing Dogs   "La Nuit" Valse, *O. Métra.*

	a. Wedding Marche (on the occasion of the Duke of York's Wedding)... *L. Wenzel.*
14. The Diamond Jubilee Procession.	14.⎰ *b.* Vercingetorix Marche ... *L. Wenzel.*
	c. Jubilee March, from "Under one Flag" Ballet ... ... *L. Wenzel.*
15. Scene taken from a Moving Train near Clapham Junction.	15. Métropolitain Galop ... *Ch. Hubans.*

THE EMPIRE ORCHESTRA, *under the direction of Monsieur* LEOPOLD WENZEL.

The Entertainment under the Management of Mr. H. J. HITCHINS.

GOD SAVE THE QUEEN.

Programme on silk of an exhibition of the Cinématographe to Queen Victoria. The list of carefully chosen musical items to accompany the film is of particular interest. Early films were often supported by the Phonograph or Pianola. (228)

⊰ PART ONE. ⊱
OVERTURE
◁ ANIMATED PHOTOGRAPHS. ▷

1. A Family Cycling Party.
2. Canadian Snow Scenes.
3. A Floral Fete.
4. A Phantom Ride.
5. H.M. The King's Entry into Dublin and Tour through Ireland.
6. A Typical Irish View.
7. Waves breaking on the Sea Shore.
8. A reminiscence of the War.
9. A Football Match.
10. A Game of Snowballing.
11. Through London on a Motor Car.

12. M. Loubert in London.
13. Opening of Parliament by H.M. The King.
14. London Streets in Sunshine.
15. London Street in a Fog.
16. Panorama of the Traffic.
17. The Gardener and the Hose.
18. March out of Volunteers.
19. Conjuring Extraordinary.
20. London's Welcome to the Crew of the "Powerful."
21. A Royal Garden Party at Buckingham Palace. (By special permission.)

An Interval of Five Minutes.

Various Views and Flower Studies from Nature,
PROJECTED BY MEANS OF
C. GOODWIN NORTON'S
PHOTOCHROMOSCOPE,

Used by him at the CRYSTAL PALACE, to illustrate the New Process of Photography in Colours.

A Cottage at Guilford, with Snowstorm—Beautiful Venice, the Rialto—A Cottage in the Wood—An Old Parish Church—St. Peter's, Rome—The Eiffel Tower (Day and Night)—Hotel De Ville, Paris—The Death of Nelson—The Sphinx and The Great Pyramids.

HUMOROUS RECITATIONS—(Illustrated.)

"The Quaker and the Robber,"
"How Bill Adams won the Battle of Waterloo
"Mystify & Co." and many others. } C. GOODWIN NORTON.

For full particulars of these, see separate list. Post Free.

⊰ PART TWO. ⊱
◁ ANIMATED PHOTOGRAPHS. ▷

The most Sensational Fire Sce
EVER CINEMATOGRAPHED.

The Film of this Picture is 500 feet long, and contains 8,000 Photographs—every one clear and distinct.

**The Outbreak—The Alarm—The Turnout of Engines
Escape—Rousing the Inmates—Exciting Rescues b
the Escape and Jumping Sheet.**

A Magnificent Picture of a State Procession in In

Russian Cavalry Charging, and Mounted Infantry Skirmishing.
A Royal Procession in India.
A Scene on the Boulevard Sevastopool, illustrating Paris on a Gala Day

22. A Minuet.
23. Santa-Claus, a Child's Dream of Christmas Eve.
24. The Durbar at Delhi.

25. A South African Transport.
26. The Distracted Bather.
27. The Wonderful Fire Scene.
28. The Butcher and the Tramp.

29. A Microbe Magnified One Million Times.
30. French Soldiers Marching.
31. Spanish Soldiers Charging.
32. Portsmouth Harbour.
33. A Country Cattle Show.

34. The "Renown" having on b T.R.H. The Prince and Prin Wales.
35. Cricket on board the Ophir.
36. The Coronation Procession.
37. Good Night.
38. God save the King.

This list is constantly being added to and brought Up-to-Date.

Most of the above were Photographed by C. Goodwin Norton, and Exhibited by hir

Amateur Projection was common during early days of the cinema. Left, a simple proj such as was used for public and private e tainment at the turn of the century. Rig similar projector used by C. Goodwin No author of an authoritative treatise on the lantern, and his son in 1896. Above, a gramme of an entertainment given by Goo Norton combining a film show with magic tern effects. (229–231)

asure and Instruction were mingled in Goodwin Norton's
grammes as in those of many of his earnest contemporaries.
vel subjects showing distant countries and peoples were
cially popular. (232, 233)

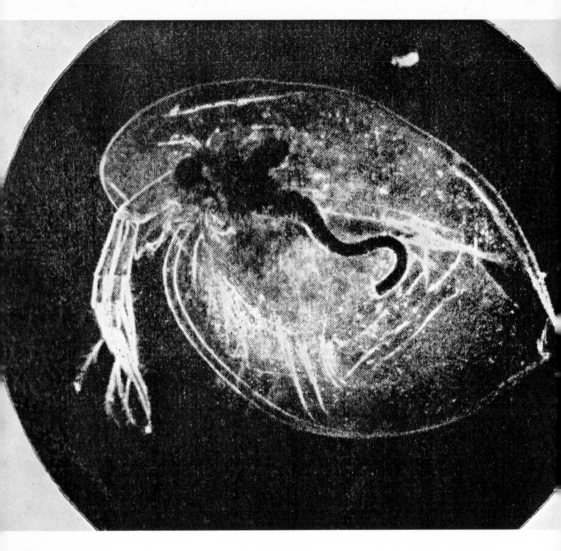

Scientific films were made before the end of the last cent
by F. Martin Duncan for Charles Urban, the American-Bri
pioneer. Duncan's films were the forerunners of the 'Secret:
Nature' series of the twenties. The future of the cinema a
world-wide industry, however, lay in the sphere of pure en
tainment. Above, frame from *The Anatomy of the Water*
(234)

There are three more names which must be cited for pioneering work in different directions. These were the French inventors, Reynaud and Méliès, and the Englishman Paul. Emile Reynaud (1844–1918), Professor of Natural Sciences, has already been mentioned as the constructor of the Praxinoscope (1876–1877). In 1882 he combined this viewing apparatus with a projector. At first he used coloured pictures on a paper roll, the background or scenic framework being cast by a second projector. From 1888 on he used long ribbons of pictures made of celluloid and perforated (single-hole perforation between the frames). The pictures were 4 x 5 centimetres in size, drawn in white on a black ground, or else tinted. On December 1, 1888, he applied for a patent, which was granted on January 14, 1889, Number B.F. 194,482,[1] for his Théâtre Optique, and on October 28, 1892, Reynaud put on his show of living pictures in the Cabinet Fantastique of the Musée Grévin on the Boulevard Montmartre in Paris.

The programme included three strips: *Un bon bock*, made in 1888–89, length 50 metres, 700 frames, time 15 minutes; *Clown et ses chiens* (1890), 22 metres, 300 frames, 10 minutes; *Pauvre Pierrot* (1891), 36 metres, 500 frames, 15 minutes. There followed later: *Un Rêve au coin du feu* (1893), 29 metres, 400 frames, 12 minutes; and *Autour d'une Cabine* (1893–1894), 45 metres, 636 frames, 15 minutes.

Between 1892 and 1900, there were a total of 12,800 performances in the Musée Grévin, attended by 500,000 visitors. The shows continued to draw customers long after genuine films were being offered in numerous cinemas. In fact Reynaud's moving pictures – which were not merely scenes, but little narratives – have a curious charm to this day. Perhaps this lies in the unreality with which the somewhat phantasmal figures move through curiously dead spaces. But Georges Sadoul is off the mark when he says:[2] 'Before we again encounter pictures as spirited, as perfect, as lasting as these, we must wait for the mature work of Walt Disney.' Such praise is eulogy but not a sober critical evaluation; it blurs the distinction between relative and absolute values.

From a relative viewpoint, Reynaud's achievement is extraordinary. He projected genuine coloured continuous pictures at a time when no one else was doing this. What was more, he attached cams to his film strips which tripped a series of electrical relays, and thus produced noises suitable to the picture being shown – at least the suggestion of sound film. But in all objectivity we must recognise that Reynaud was a mediocre draughtsman, a charming visionary, but hardly an artist. His strong sense of individuality deterred him from taking up cinematography, and when he went into it, much too late, he attempted too much, experimented with stereoscopic films, and failed. The French expression *dessins animés* has been taken over into English; but in Reynaud's case it must be taken literally as meaning only 'animated drawings'; for his *Pantomimes Lumineuses* shown in the Musée Grévin were not photographed strips, as are Disney's 'animated cartoons'.

Nevertheless, he deserves all our sympathy, for he was an unlucky man who was outstripped by nimbler-minded competitors. One evening in 1910 in a fit of severe melancholy over his failure to achieve any outward success, he dumped most of his films and apparatus into the Seine.[3] In 1918 he died in a sanatorium in Ivry.

A man who in many respects had more of a gift for coping with life, and who as a talented conjurer opened up new avenues for the film, came to almost as sad an end.

Georges Méliès (1861–1938) started out as a mechanic, actor, cartoonist, stage-designer. He then learned the art of magic from the famous Robert-Houdin. In 1888 he took over the direction of the Théâtre Robert-Houdin. He was the first to see the possibilities of the Lumières' invention for a new type of showmanship. He made an offer;[4] it was rejected. In his memoirs he artlessly reports his next steps:[5] 'Méliès ... seeks, combines, himself constructs his first camera, and a month later projects his first films and opens the first public cinema in the world in the Théâtre Robert-Houdin.'

He did everything himself. He was, as he himself attested, '*dessinateur, décorateur, illusioniste, auteur de scénario, metteur en scène et artiste principal de toutes ses compositions*'.

195

From 1896–1914 he produced a vast number of films (they must have totalled some 4000). The firm of Georges Méliès, Star Film became widely known; as early as 1904 a New York branch was opened. We have a Complete Catalogue of 1905, which bears the notice: 'All our films are copyrighted'. In Class I he offers the American market 421 different film strips (delivery time, four weeks). Number 1: *Playing Cards;* Numbers 420–21: *Drunkard and Inventor.* The average length of these films: 65 feet; price, $ 9.75. In Class II he offered 'secondary negatives' for 13 cents per foot, including *Cinderella,* 410 feet in length, which cost $ 53.50 – 'a grand spectacular production ... in which over thirty-five people take part'. This was followed immediately by a *Joan of Arc,* 815 feet in length, a film involving more than 500 actors. Number 312–13 was a $ 17 item called *Going to Bed under Difficulties* and described as 'very funny':

'A Traveller puts up in an inn. He hangs his overcoat and hat upon a peg in his room, but he finds, instantly, that his clothes are on his back again. He takes off his coat a second time, but it instantly returns. He becomes enraged. The more rapidly he undresses, the more rapidly his clothes go back to his body. He rolls on the floor, then on the bed, and finally has an epileptic fit.'

Moreover, Méliès was working only with his own capital. 'Who else can say that?' he asked, not without justice. He handled all forms, produced: '*Drame, comédie, vaudeville, opéra, opéra-comique, operette, vues à trucs, vues de voyages fantastiques, documentaires, actualités, etc.*' He was called – he cites the epithets with pride – *Roi de la Fantasmagorie, Jules Verne du Cinéma, Magicien de l'Écran.*

In 1900 he became president of the first Chambre Syndicale des Éditeurs Cinématographiques. He held that post until 1912. But by then his inventive powers were exhausted; the international cinema had moved in other directions, and Méliès was forgotten.

In the Thirties an avant-garde theatre director discovered the resigned old man eking out a scant living as proprietor of a kiosk selling souvenirs at the Montparnasse railroad station in Paris. We have a letter of the septuagenarian, dated June 27, 1932, one of the most moving documents in the annals of the cinema.[6] And now his work underwent a resurrection. Innumerable papers were written on it. His old films were collected. Chaplin called him the 'alchemist of light'. D. W. Griffith declared: 'I owe everything to him'. Jean Cocteau spent days studying Méliès' old strips before setting to work on his own. These admirers succeeded in obtaining a small pension for Méliès. The recognition came too late – he died on June 21, 1938.

French historians of the cinema now feel it their patriotic duty to praise his work – without defining his limits. Working when he did, at the turn of the century, his accomplishments were indeed extraordinary; today they are curiosities. Whatever his theme, he approached it as a magician, a prestidigitator of the stage. He was a pioneer in the possibilities of cinematic technique only insofar as such techniques could be carried out by décor and props; he produced not trick films, but filmed tricks.[7] Of course his 'tricks in films' were a sortie into unexplored country. But he did not create any of the things that were later to be regarded as specifically cinematic. With a 'camera set in concrete' he filmed his clever contrivances and did not dream of how subtle details are added to make a scene, scenes added to make events, and events welded into a plot. His narratives of strange adventures (he did almost every one of Jules Verne's science-fiction stories) were arranged in tableaux; they were neither acts nor scenes, but numbers in a magic show; and what he created was neither drama nor comedy, but always – regarded from the standpoint of form – a series of sensationel variety items.

All the same, we must pay homage to his superabundant imagination. For *Quat' Cents Coups du Diable* (444 metres, 35 tableaux, coloured, 1906) he built a parallelogram of beams which went up two stories in order to show the devil's carriage in proper movement; the artificial horse was suspended by ropes which were manipulated by five workmen in the attic of the structure. For *À la Conquête du Pôle* he constructed an Ice Giant of wood and wire. Some twenty stagehands were needed to work the monster, but it could blink its eyes, move arms and fingers. Each of his films contained a number of such tours de force. In one, a man kept growing new heads as he tossed his old heads into the air, where they remained hanging in telegraph wires as musical notes *(Le Mélomane)*. In another, the moon wept a plump tear because the bold explorers' space ship had just landed in its eye (*Le Voyage dans la Lune*, 1902); or a man with a bellows pumped up the head of a living man until it was as large as a wardrobe (*L'Homme à la Tête de Caoutchouc*, 1897); in another Méliès appeared as an actor and actually confronted himself – the first double rôle.[8] Finally he filmed 'newsreels' – doing studio reconstructions of *L'Eruption du Mont Pelée* and *La Catastrophe de Maine*! He made the first detective film (*L'Histoire d'un Crime*, 1899) and one of the first monster spectaculars (*La Prophétesse de Thèbes*, 1907) in wild extravagances of colours.

He had the audacity of the inspired dilettante. But he never rose above the level of the magic show; his scenarios stagger us by their naiveté. Therein lay his ultimate failure. When, shortly before the First World War, the first cinema dramas and epics appeared, the conjurer had to step off the stage.

Robert William Paul[9] was a completely different type. A skilled English optician, he entered the field of cinematography under less than honourable circumstances when he discovered that Edison's device was protected by patents everywhere in the world except England. He thereupon yielded to the urging of two Greek entrepreneurs and shamelessly reconstructed the apparatus for them. Yet he promptly went beyond the Edison Kinetoscope by attempting to project his pictures, and as early as February 1896 gave the first performance of his Theatrograph at the Finsbury Technical College.

Edison attempted to worst the thief by holding back the supply of film strips which Paul had blandly requested. But Paul sensed what was in the wind (on February 20, 1896, Trewey had begun showing Lumière films at the London Regent Polytechnic, and had scored a great success), and energetically proceeded to make his own film strips with his own camera. In 1899 he had a studio at New Southgate. His first strip was *Rough Sea at Dover* (1896). He made a newsreel of the final spurt in the Derby at Epsom. This won him a four-year contract with the Alhambra; he was to fill out every programme with fifteen minutes of films.

In 1898 the average length of his films was 40–80 feet – up to one and a quarter minutes of running time. By 1902 they had increased to 100 feet (one and two-thirds minutes running time), by 1906, 650 feet (eleven minutes). He would turn out some fifty films per year – not many, compared to the production of others; but his films were extraordinarily successful. He always remained more of a technician than a producer, rapidly freed himself from Edison's models and introduced significant improvements. Probably he was the first to achieve success in projection with a seven-point Maltese Cross. He also, though only by the by, brought a large number of new subjects to the screen. He did adventure films, trick films, ghost films, comics, newsreels.[10] In fact, he would deserve to be called the English Méliès, were it not that he lacked the magician's brilliant dilettantism. He was partial to trick photography: in *A Railway Collision* (1898) toy trains plunged into abysses; a skeleton haunted *Undressing Extraordinary* (1901–1902); in *The ? Motorist* (1905) the pursued automobile runs right up the wall of a building, into the clouds, and once around the sun. Possibly Paul was the first to demonstrate the most uncanny power of the cinema, the power of propaganda, when in 1900 he turned out some twenty films on *Army Life, or How Soldiers are Made.*[11]

Notes to the text

1 Patent description with illustrations in *Emile Reynaud* (Cinématèque française, 1945). The life and work of Reynaud is also treated in detail in this work. In the literature of the cinema, it is common for two different dates to be mentioned for one and the same patent. This is due to the fact that because of possible disputes, both the application date and the day of the actual issue of the patent are noted. In case of disputes, the postmark date of application may decide priority; hence, the first date is decisive for the lawyers. For historians and biographers a still earlier date may be crucial. See Jungmann: *Das internationale Patentrecht*, 1924.

2 From *Emile Reynaud*, p. 24.

3 See the memoirs of his son Paul Reynaud in: *Emile Reynaud, Peintre de Film*, p. 26.

4 For Lumière's reply, see the quotation, p. 11.

5 *Mes mémoires*, reprinted in Bessy and Duca, *Georges Méliès, Mage*. The memoirs contain numerous inaccuracies.

6 In the archives of Carl Vincent, Brussels; partially printed in Bessy and Duca: *Georges Méliès, Mage*, p. 192.

7 Only a few times did he utilise the optical possibilities provided by camera and film: double exposure, mirror tricks.

8 German books on the subject call Paul Wegener (together with Guido Seeber) the 'inventor' of the double role. That is incorrect; it was probably Méliès, if not someone else before him. But the Frenchman showed only a single trick; Wegener, in the *Student von Prag* (1913) gave the trick dramaturgic dimensions.

9 1869–1943. So far as I know, no special studies of him have been published. Precise data in Low and Manvell: *The History of the British Film 1896–1906* (1948). A gold mine for amusing anecdotes of those days is F. A. Talbot's *Moving Pictures* (1912).

10 The principal catalogues of *Paul's Animatograph Works, Ltd.* appeared in 1901, 1902 and 1906. Unfortunately, their arrangement is not chronological.

11 The War Office testified to the propaganda value of these films for future recruiting drives. Since the strips dealt with the actual life of soldiers, Paul rightly regarded them at the time as 'newsreels' – whereas nowadays we could call them (depending on our point of view) documentary or propaganda pictures. Incidentally, Cecil Hepworth produced two similar series that same year: *The British Army* and *The British Navy*. Two other Englishman should be mentioned. G. A. Smith (born in 1864), originally a portrait photographer, was the first to develop numerous film tricks (in contrast to Méliès' 'tricks in the film'). He recognised the possibilities of the mobile camera, of the close-up, of the cut. He became head of the so-called

Brighton School, whose realistic open-air scenes influenced Continental moviemakers. Then there is James Williamson (1855–1933), owner of a pharmacy, amateur photographer, who went into film production together with his entire family. In *Two Naughty Boys* (1897) and *Attack on a Chinese Mission Station, Fire!* (1901), he attempted the first dramatically complete story films.

The Biophonograph represents an essential aspect of the ea days of the commercial cinema when the moving picture v often combined with the phonograph to produce a 'talkie'. (2

e **commercial success** of the cinema as a mass entertainment was foreshadowed by Emile
ⁱnaud's *Théâtre Optique*. Reynaud had already projected the images on the glass plates of
Praxinoscope in 1882, using a lampascope to provide the background and another lantern
ⁱast the motion effects on the screen (top left). From 1892 he painted the images on trans-
ent perforated celluloid and used rear projection with the apparatus concealed behind the
en (left). Reynaud was the first to introduce spools to handle the film on a commercially prac-
l basis. He also realised the supreme attraction of the narrative film and accompanied his
ures with specially written music and synchronized sound effects. Between 1892 and 1900
,000 persons saw the Théâtre Optique which was presented twice daily. Left, a scene from
vre Pierrot; above, scene from *Clown et ses Chiens*. (236–238)

All the fantastic possibilities of the
mière invention were grasped by Geo
Méliès, a professional magician befor
opened his cinema in the Théâtre Ro
Houdin, which he had acquired in 1
Above, Méliès makes the same actor (h
self) appear twice on the screen for
first time. Left, Méliès' studio at Montre
and right, Méliès directing his film
Boleyn. (239–241)

The trick of doubling is again brilliantly used in *The Indiarubber Head*, once more featuring Méliès himself. Méliès acting in his own film *A la Conquête du Pôle* with background painted by himself (left). (242–244)

Within the image: COPYRIGHTED / BY GEO. MÉLIÈS 1906 / Paris New York

The past and future of optical entertainment meet in Méli[...]
exuberant creations. His screen adaptations of fairy tales, [...]
which *Bluebeard* (right) is one of many, continue the traditi[...]
established by the 'Ombres Chinoises'. His scenes of stupend[...]
catastrophe, of which *Les Quatre Cents Coups du Diable* (abo[...]
is but one of innumerable examples, combining painting a[...]
photography, recall many Diorama effects and set the fash[...]
for this typical feature of the slapstick comedy film. Méli[...]
Histoire d'un Crime (top right) is the prototype of the realis[...]
crime film. (245–247)

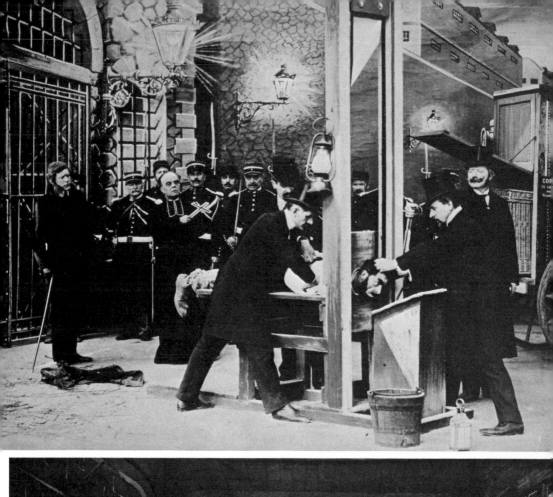

COPYRIGHTED
BY GEO. MÉLIÈS 1906
PARIS NEW YORK
Trade-Mark ★ film

poetic and ingenuous quality rarely found in the commercial cinema transforms all the crudeness and flamboyance of
Méliès' films. *La Prophétesse de Thèbes*, first spectacular film
'epic', the *Voyage dans la Lune*, first science fiction film, based on
the novel by Jules Verne, and *A Visit to the Sirens of Neptune*,
first film fantasia, surpass all their successors in the imaginative
power with which the visual effects peculiar to the screen – the
incredible, the droll and the crazy – have been exploited. (248
to 250)

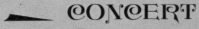

PROGRAMME

OF THE

Cheltenham Cricket Club

AND

CONCERT

AND

LIST OF PICTURES OF

PAUL'S THEATROGRAPH

(Animated Photographs).

ESDAY, DECEMBER 1st, 1896, at Eight o'clock.

Patrons:

THE MAYOR (Colonel Rogers).

SER, J. T., Esq., J.P.	GLADWYN, H. FAIR, Esq.	PAYNE, MAJOR SELWYN
INGHAM, W., Esq.	HATTERSLEY-SMITH, REV. P. H.	ROBERTSON, J. L., Esq.
ISS	HALL, J., Esq., C.E.	ROXBY, REV. E. L.
P. W., Esq.	HORLICK, J., Esq.	RUSSELL, COLONEL, M.P.
OLMORE, W. B.; Esq.	KAY, SIR BROOK, BART.	SKILLICORNE, W. N., Esq., J.P.
RES, BARON	MELLERSH, W. H., Esq.	VASSAR-SMITH, R. V., Esq., J.P.
F., Esq., J.P.	NELSON-FOSTER, T., Esq., J.P.	WARD-HUMPHREYS, DR.

TICKETS 2/6 (Reserved), **1/-**, Back Seats **6d.**

y be obtained and Plan of Room may be seen at Woodward's Music Warehouse, Promenade Cheltenham.

Robert Paul, British pioneer of the motion picture, duplicated Edison's Kinetoscope, invented a cine-camera to take films for it and devised a projector in 1895. It was demonstrated at the Royal Institute on February 28th 1896. Paul's entertainment, called the 'Theatrograph', was shown in the same year at the Olympia, the Alhambra, where it ran for four years, and in all the principal towns of England. Paul's cine-camera of 1896 (left) was provided with a specially designed stand to keep passing objects in view, a device which came to be extensively adopted. Paul's studio, at Sydney Road, New Southgate, built in 1899 (below) was the first of its type in Europe. It had a glass roof and sliding doors and was equipped for trick effects. An unusual feature at that date was the mobile camera. (251–254)

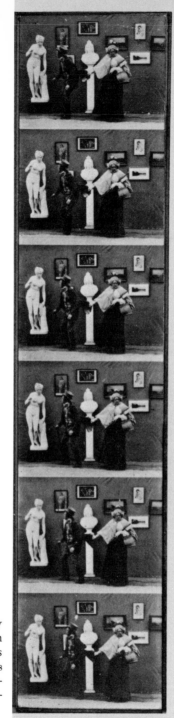

Kinetoscope film strips made by R. W. Paul 1896–97 for use in his own peephole instrument based on Edison's device. He used perforated film 1³/₈ inches wide. These films were afterwards projected by means of the Theatrograph. (255–258)

The special properties of the mo
picture were exploited by Paul as
were by Méliès in films of extrava
buffoonery, violence, magic and
supernatural. Stills from *Come a
Do*, 1897, *Her Brave Defender*
Undressing Extraordinary, 1896; r
stills from *The Magic Sword*, 1
and *Railway Collision*, 1898, the
film to show disaster by mean
miniature models. Paul's films
later shown by Pathé. (259–263)

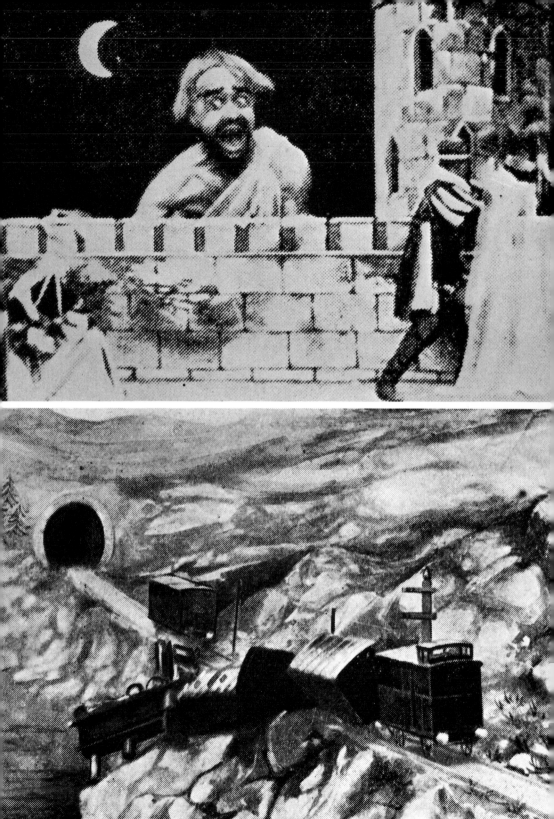

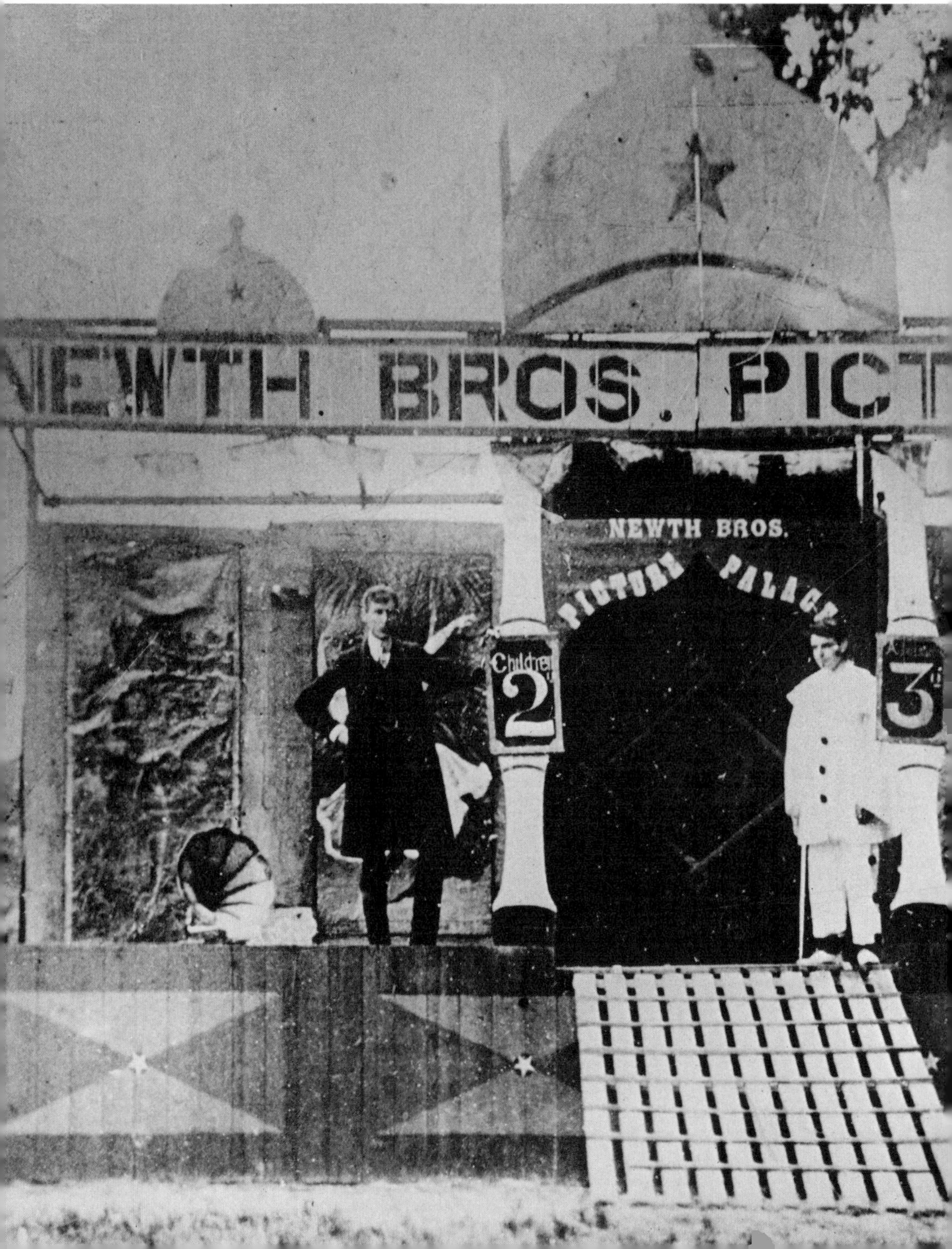
NEWTH BROS. PICT
NEWTH BROS.
PICTURE PALACE
Children
2
3

The transformation of the motion picture from a scientific amusement into a world-wide industry started when it became a regular commercial form of entertainment. Cinema Theatres were unknown for the first decade after Lumière's demonstration of the Cinématographe. Travelling showmen, of whom the Newth brothers (left) were representative, would exhibit at fairgrounds up and down the country, many of them devising their own equipment and writing, producing and acting in their own films. Walter Haggar, whose booth appears below, was one of the best known of these showmen-producers. Some pioneering showmen organized film entertainments in empty shops. The projectionist in Knübbel's 1903 Berlin 'shop cinema' (below) is holding a spool. The programme, it is interesting to note, was changed twice weekly. (264–266)

Another typical showman of the pioneer period was Frank Mottershaw, here seen setting out with his family in 1896 for their round of cinematograph displays. Mottershaw was the owner of a photographic business in Sheffield and a well known magic lanternist before he took to cinematography. This isolated provincial showman eventually gained an international reputation; he had agencies all over the world and sold many of his films to American syndicates. Among Frank Mottershaw's many successful productions was *The Life of Charles Peace*, a scene from which is shown below. It was technically one of the most advanced films of the time. The subject, based on events in the career of the famous criminal, was also treated by Walter Haggar. (267, 268)

great names of the stage were often associated with the
:ma in the days when anonymity shrouded the screen player
per. At his Phono-Ciné Theatre in the Paris Exhibition of
), Clement Maurice showed film versions of Sarah Bernhardt
:cenes from *Hamlet,* Coquelin in a scene from *Cyrano de
;erac* and Little Tich in some of his variety turns. Phono-
ph and motion picture were synchronized in this entertain-
ts. Above, French fashions, 1897. (269, 270)

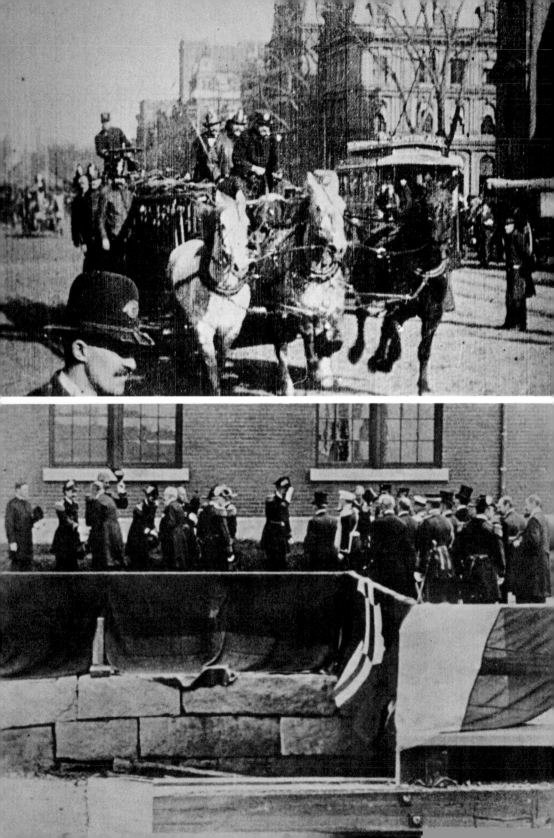

ws items were an important at-
ction in the first public screen
ws. Left, the New York Fire Brigade
1897 and Admiral Dewey landing
Gibraltar, Edison films; right, the
eral of Queen Victoria, 1901. (271
73)

Actuality and topical films were an early speciality of Cecil Hepworth who is seen here photographing from the top of a bus in 1900. Hepworth, the son of a famous lanternist, began by making arc lamps for Paul's Theatrograph and was the author, in 1897, of *The ABC of Cinematography*. Later he evolved the first film developing machine, the ancestor of the devices which have eliminated hand processing in the great film laboratories of today. (274)

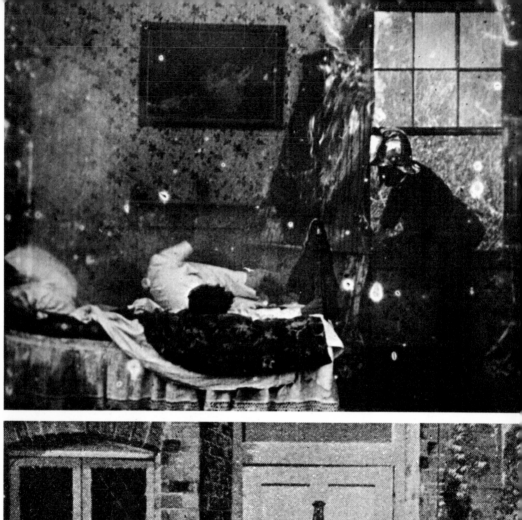

THE JEWEL THIEVES OUTWITTED

Presenting –
Mr JACK HULCUP &
Mrs VIOLET HOPSON

THE PURSUIT BY AEROPLANE

SPECIAL NOTICE
This Poster is sold on Condition
that it is only to be used to
advertise the "HEPWORTH"
FILM to which it refers.

CHORLEY & PICKERSGILL LTD THE ELECTRIC PRESS LEEDS & LONDON

The Story picture soon proved to be more popular than either topical films or the brief strips of prize fights, music hall turns and screen tricks with which the public had at first been satisfied. A scene from James Williamson's *Fire!*, 1901, one of the most elaborate and sensational of the early narrative films. Left, Cecil Hepworth, made up as a burglar, appears in his first story film of 1901. Poster for a thriller distributed by the Hepworth Manufacturing Company which Hepworth had founded with R. V. Lawley in 1899. (275–277)

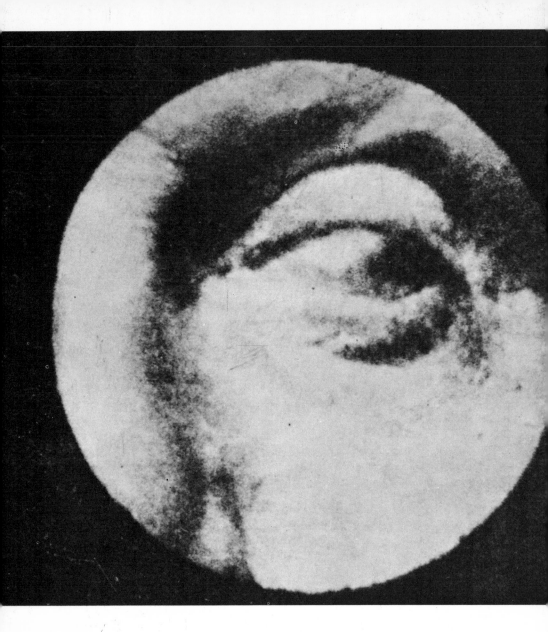

The so-called Brighton School consisted principally of J. W. liamson who wrote, produced and acted in his own films at Lodge, Hove and G. A. Smith, a life-long colleague of Cha Urban, who began as a Brighton portrait photographer and the inventor in 1908 of Kinemacolor. Close-up from G Smith's *Grandma's Reading Glass:* grandma's eye as seen by little grandson through the reading glass. Smith's studio a Anne's Well Gardens and, inside, a set from *Mary Jane's Mis* 1901. The films of both Smith and Williamson were distrib by Gaumont. (278–280)

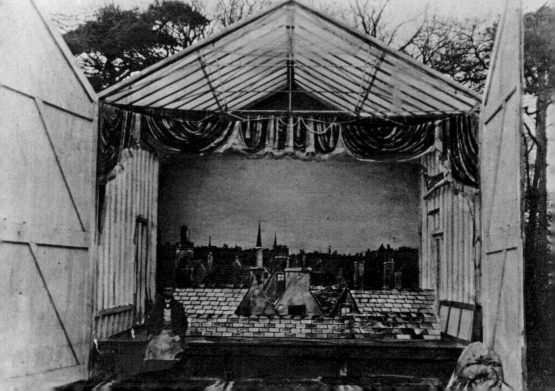

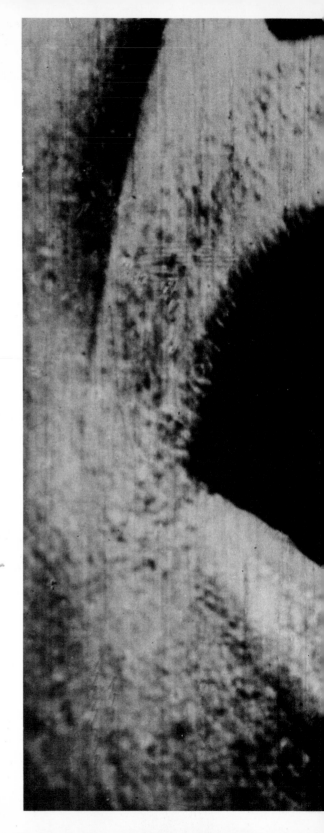

The interpolated close-up was used by G. A. Smith as early as 1900. In *A Big Swallow* a man's face is brought closer and closer to the spectator until the screen is covered by his open mouth. This effect differed from the existing use of the close-up in the popular 'facials' in that it did not consist of a single shot but of a general view in which was cut a close-up of some particular object. (281)

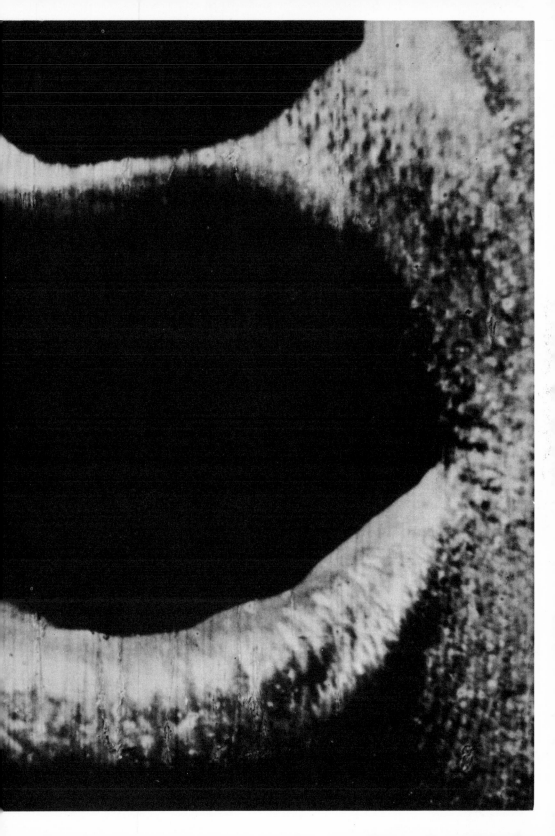

Two characteristic films of G. A. Smith, the fantasy *Dorothy's Dream* and (below) the melodrama *The Little Witness* both of which made use of trick photography. Smith's first trick films preceded those of R. W. Paul and anticipated much of Méliès' work. (282, 283)

The film industry owed much to the work of Charles Pathé in France and Oskar Messter in Germany. Messter evolved a projector achieving intermittent movement by means of the Maltese Cross which came to replace the claw movement of the Lumière apparatus in all commercial projectors. Left, still from an early Messter narrative film *Das Gewissen*, 1903; below, still from Pathé's *Le Plongeur fantastique*, directed by Zecca, the first film to make use of reversed movement. (284, 285)

Among the first stars of the screen was the French comedian Max
Linder, shown here in *La Vie de Polichinelle*, a farce in the Commedia
dell' Arte tradition directed by Ferdinand Zecca, formerly a music hall
singer, for Pathé in 1905. Below, Charles Pathé (right) and Zecca.
Right, Pathé poster from the period immediately preceding the first
World War when Pathé films covered the globe. (286–288)

Italy's main contribution to the ex
panding film industry was the spec
tacular costume piece. *The Last Day*
of Pompeii (1908) was the first of
series of such films made by Artur
Ambrosio, a former optician who bui
a studio in Turin in partnership wit
Pasquali. (289)

The cult of the screen idol, the i
evitable accompaniment of the cor
mercialized cinema, began in earne
with the unprecedented success of As
Nielsen in *Abgründe* 1910, directed l
Urban Gad. Here and in *Der Stude*
von Prag, with Paul Wegener, film
by Guido Seeber, stardom has not a
together obscured the individuality
the actor. But in the American 'st
system' the actor became a figure
synthesis, shaped by the director. Bet
Blythe (right) was 'made' by her c
rector J. Gordon Edwards. (290-29

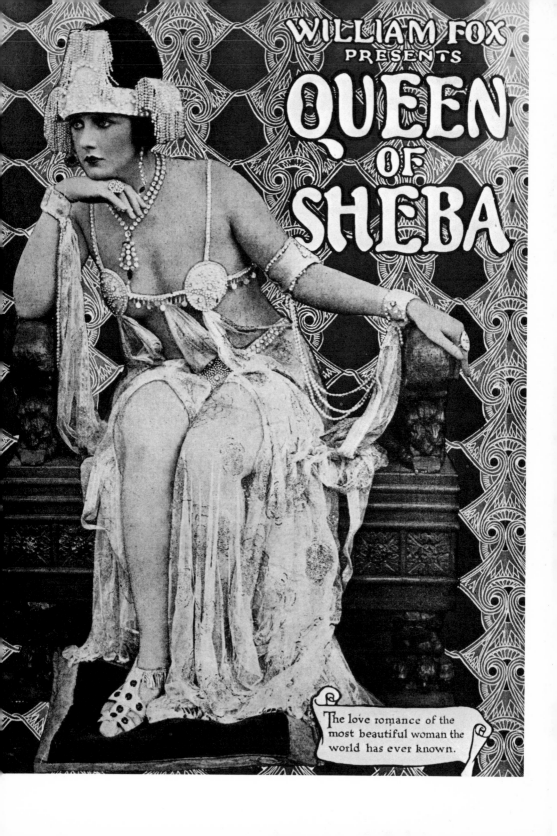

The brightest star in the whole screen galaxy, the greatest box office draw, Charlie Chaplin, was also, paradoxically, one of the few who succeeded entirely in realizing himself in a medium altogether subservient to industry. (293)

The long lines of people in front of the cinematographic show-booths grew longer. A few bold entrepreneurs rented permanent quarters – empty coal cellars, vacant greengrocers' shops. The bolder ones wrote the word *Theatre* over the entrance. The cinema had been born. It demanded nourishment. Those were days of economic boom, of growing mass-mindedness, of urbanisation and rapid population growth. Classes whose entertainment had been limited to trashy novels found in these living pictures a gratification of demands which, for them, were just as 'cultural' as the demand of the higher classes for stage plays. And they craved that gratification more and more insistently.[1]

This direct demand for gratification was translated into an indirect demand upon the men who were to provide new 'material' for it. These men were expected to create ex nihilo something that did not yet exist: more and more raw film, more and more cameras and projectors, more and more studios with more and more technicians and actors, and more and more new ideas.

These men had one characteristic in common: They combined in themselves virtually all the functions that were essential to bring moving pictures to a public. They were at once inventors, constructors, cameramen, directors; they developed their own films, copied them, sold them, and even projected them themselves. It must have been apparent to most of them that they had been cast into the predicament of the sorcerer's apprentice. Either they hunted for new magic spells, found them, and survived; or else they were consumed by the blaze of light they themselves had kindled.

The competition that began in 1896 was hectic and hellish. A headstart of three months could make a film producer rich, could spell ruin to his rivals.

At the very time the first inventor and producer was commencing on his crucial work in Germany, the brothers Lumière presented their fellow-countryman Charles Pathé[2] with finished apparatus and film strips. With that headstart, Pathé became the first international 'cinema czar', who for more than a decade dominated all of Europe, and for a while America as well.

Charles Pathé (born in 1863) was certainly one of the great figures of the period. One of six children, the son of a butcher, he grew up first in Chevry-Cossigny, then in Vincennes, reluctantly learned his father's trade, and set out for Argentina to make his fortune. An epidemic of yellow fever drove him back to France after two years. He returned poor as a church mouse. The turning point in his life came in October 1894. In Vincennes he saw shows given with Edison machines, and heard that the showman earned more in four hours than he did in a week. He raised two thousand francs and installed an Edison apparatus in Monthéty; according to his own story, if the enterprise proved a fiasco, he would not have had enough money to pay for a return ticket to Vincennes. When he finally felt the inclination to return, after countless performances, he could well afford his fare. In 1895 he joined forces with the inventor Marie-Henry-Joseph Joly (born in 1866),[3] constructed motion picture apparatus of his own, and his rocketlike rise began.

In a Napoleonic gesture, he took his three brothers, Émile, Théophile and Jacques, into the business. In 1896 Pathé Frères was founded – its aim, at first, only to build cameras and projectors. In December 1897 he set up the Pathé Cinéma for producing films – by now he must already have had licenses from the Lumières. In 1898 his first film appeared: *L'Arrivée d'un train de Vincennes*. He had successful man's knack for finding talented associates, and soon came upon Ferdinand Zecca, who was to be recognised as the first distinguished film director. There followed *Histoire d'une Crime*, *L'École du Malheur* (1902) and Zecca's best known strips, *Le Plongeur fantastique* (1903), and *La Passion du Christ* (1905). Also in 1905 he produced *La Vie de Polichinelle*, which featured Max Linder, the comedian who rose to world fame with Pathé. There were hundreds of others. The Gallic cock, the insignia of the firm of Pathé, became familiar to every child in Europe and throughout the world. A few figures to mark the stages of success: The firm was founded with a capital of 24,000 francs. This rose to 1,000,000 francs in 1899, 2,000,000 in 1900, 2,666,000 in 1901, 3,200,000 in 1905, 3,800,000 in 1907, 5,000,000 in 1908, 15,000,000 in 1911, 30,000,000 in 1913.

Pathé's own proudly modest comment on this achievement was: '*Je n'ai pas inventé le cinéma, mais je l'ai industrialisé!*'

Another of the major figures of those early years was Oskar Messter (1866–1944). His father was a Berlin mechanic who had established his own optical business at the age of nineteen, and who devoted his evenings to giving shows with 'dissolving view devices'[4] of his own construction. The son entered his father's business at eighteen, took over the firm at twenty-six and began making his own small inventions. In 1891 Oskar Messter became interested in the Anschütz Tachyscope. In 1895 he recognised the possibilities of the Edison Kinetoscope. Until then he had been merely an ambitious young man. But now the spark struck flame. In April 1896 he saw the first cinematographic projections in Berlin, and succumbed to the new medium with heart and soul and all his money. He obtained Edison film strips from London, and on June 15, 1896, after weeks of feverish work, he delivered to a Russian showman, at a price of 1900 marks, the first practical independently constructed projector.

But the word 'independently' must be taken with a grain of salt; it cannot be accepted in the sweeping sense that German historians, who repeat Messter's own claim, have used it.[5] The projector had already been invented many times over in other countries. Messter had seen what there was to see; he had even had an English projector in his shop for repair. He had put his eye to all the keyholes. Moreover, without the Edison films he would not even have had the wherewithal to experiment. In addition, the Skladanowskys had already made projections in Germany itself, although with apparatus that had no future. Messter is less than honest when, in the section of his memoirs[6] dealing with this early period, he does not even mention the Skladanowskys. He is, however, entitled to complete credit for substituting the Maltese Cross[7] for the claw movement of the Lumière projector. The Maltese Cross provides the necessary intermittent movement of the pictures inside the projector by means of a tangential grip and to this day remains a component of all projectors. And he gave proof of remarkable originality when, intending to produce his own films and lacking a camera, he used the reel of his projector to hold the raw film and transformed his *entire living room* into a camera obscura by darkening it and leaving only a tiny hole for light from the street to enter. In actual fact he achieved his first real, continuous films by this method.

He can be hailed as the German Pathé, not so much for his apparatus, but for his early perception that it was necessary to create an industry. And he created one, with incredible rapidity, if not on the French scale. Right at the start he recognised the drawbacks he laboured under. As he states simply in his memoirs:

'In order to free myself from this insecurity, I constructed a camera and after a good many toilsome experiments assembled the necessary equipment for the developing and copying of the films. That done, by the end of 1896, we had the basis for building a cinema and film industry in Germany which would operate entirely with German apparatus.'

By 1897 he was already involved in patent disputes with Pathé over the German market. The matter was settled by his being allowed to supply Greman apparatus for the German affiliates of Pathé. From 1896 to 1913 he developed seventeen versions of his projectors, rapidly adding improvement after improvement. The maximum sale, however, was only five hundred of any one model. Pathé, on the other hand, developed only three models, but he sold 70,000 of them (according to Messter's own figures).

In October 1897 (the speed is breathtaking) his first German cinema catalogue appeared, illustrated, with no less than 115 pages. He offered 84 'numbers': 'Street scenes and historical pictures, also the first German humouristic scenes[8] as well as cultural and propaganda pictures.' And discoursing on the cultural value of the cinema, he saw far into the future:

'By its means historical events can henceforth be preserved just as they happened and brought to view again not only now, but also for the benefit of future generations. Dancers, fencers, acrobats, jugglers and gymnasts everywhere can be shown performing. Elemental events and natural wonders, such as Niagara Falls, the Rhine Falls, the Giessbach, will be put before our eyes true to nature, and also the lives and customs of the most distant primitives and tribes of savages. Specialists of speed photography have already been sent out to all continents for that purpose.'

Before the First World War, Messter films and the newsreel he founded, the Messter Week, had been shown in: Germany, Austria, Denmark, Sweden, Holland, Dutch East Indies, England and her colonies, United States, South America, Italy, Spain, Portugal, Russia, Japan, Rumania, Bulgaria, Serbia, Greece, France, Belgium, Switzerland.

At this point Cinema began – and this account of its beginnings ends. Pathé and Messter stand as representatives of the infant industry which grew so rapidly after 1896. R. W. Paul and C. Hepworth in England, the great American producers Laemmle, Goldwyn, Lasky and Zukor, came later. Hollywood did not spring up until 1912. People began discussing the cinema as an art in 1913. In Germany such discussion arose in connection with the films of Paul Wegener (and we have only to see those films today to realize how absurd that all was); in America, with more justification, in connection with the post-1915 films of David Wark Griffith. The first aesthetics of the cinema was formulated by the American poet Vachel Lindsay in 1915 *(The Art of the Moving Picture)*, the first theory of cinematic art by the Hungarian Béla Balász in 1924 *(The Visible Man)*. The cinema as an art *form* was discovered by the Russians Eisenstein and Pudovkin in the early 1920's.

What has come of it all?

A Czech cinema artist, Berthold Bartosch, produced a film many years ago in which a magic parchment plays a part. A thinker had written the grand word *Freedom* on it. The sheet of parchment rises into the air and courses over the world. Evil and oppressive forces try to seize it, because the word alone seems blasphemous to them. But in vain.

A French writer, the critic and director Jean Bénoit-Lévy, took up this idea in 1945. He closed his book, *Les Grandes Missions du Cinéma*, by comparing the magic power of the cinema with the power of this parchment and prophesying that the cinema will ultimately cast so powerful a glow of light upon the idea of justice, freedom and fraternity that men will one day find themselves in a better world in which there are no longer any barriers to the free development of the human spirit.

Ah well...

1 P. von Werder: *Literatur im Bann der Verstädterung* (1943). The classical works on this subject are Ortega y Gasset: *Revolt of the Masses* (1931); David Riesman: *The Lonely Crowd;* B. Rosenberg and D. M. White: *Mass Culture* (1957). An attempt to relate birth of the cinema to social history was made by W. Panowsky in *Die Geburt des Films* (1944): 'In 1895, the year the cinema was born, more than 35 million persons in Germany belonged to the working class, and only 12.5 millions to the petty bourgeoisie. This new class of the population, which grew up in the metropolis barren of tradition, either found the traditional places of amusement barred to them allegedly for class reasons, or did not find such places to their tastes.' He rightly draws attention to the sudden appearance of grand sporting spectacles, *circenses* like soccer games, bicycle races, ice hockey matches, trotting races and boxing matches.

2 Pierre Robin: 'Cinquante ans de Cinéma Pathé' in *La Cinématographie Française*, N° 1239, 1947, pp. 33 ff. Also in this issue: 'La Production de Charles Pathé'; 'Pathé dans le monde'; 'Charles Pathé: Industriel et constructeur'.

3 Their first conversation is recorded by M. Noverre in Sadoul: *Histoire Générale* ... I, p. 188. There, too, Joly's share in the invention is discussed in detail as against that

of the Lumières. On the problem of priority claims, see also the memoirs of the inventor Grimoin Sanson (born 1860): *Le Film de ma vie* (1926).

4 Perfected magic lantern. By employing a double projector, the pictures were dissolved one into another, giving the impression of present-day 'panning'. See Musschenbroek and Child.

5 Messter: *Mein Weg mit dem Film* (1936).

6 He later mentions them as 'still unknown to me at the time of the sale of my apparatus'. It is highly improbable that this man would have overlooked the Wintergarten performances which ran for weeks, were widely publicised in advertisements and the subject of lively commentary in the newspapers. In May 1938 I had the opportunity to question Messter about the matter. He vehemently asserted his claim to be the only independent inventor and had only deprecatory comments to make about the Skladanowskys. From the polemics, it becomes clear that these old men, whose life work lay decades behind them, seem to have felt an unrelenting hatred for one another.

7 But that, too, is more a matter of perfecting than inventing. However, he does make it credible that he knew nothing about earlier devices, the 'Croix de Malte inversé' of Grimoin-Sanson, and the 'Double Croix de Malte' of Robert W. Paul. See Sadoul: *Histoire générale . . .* I, pp. 186 ff.

8 This is correct insofar as his scenes, in contrast to those presented by the Skladanowskys, showed *progressive* action.

BIBLIOGRAPHY

For primary sources on the prehistory and early history of the cinema, we must turn to the patents and catalogues of the inventors. A number of museums, such as the Deutsches Museum in Munich, the Cinématèque Française in Paris, the Barnes Museum of Cinematography, St Ives, and the Lytton Center in Hollywood possess examples of early apparatus. Contemporary newspaper accounts are, for the most part, useful only from the point of view of cultural history; the journalists had only the scantiest and sometimes most erroneous notion of the technical aspects. The catalogues of early producers from 1896 on, frequently illustrated and provided with introductions on technical matters, offer much information on early films.

In addition to the works mentioned in the 'Notes to the Text', much material is available in general works on the complete history of the cinema. The fullest and most thorough book remains Georges Sadoul's *Histoire générale du Cinéma* in four volumes (Paris, 1948–52; I: L'Invention du Cinéma 1832–1897; II: Les Pionniers du Cinéma 1897–1909; III and IV: Le Cinéma devient un art 1909–1920). Proverbial German thoroughness is best represented by Friedrich von Zglinicki: *Der Weg des Films* (Berlin, 1956). The most detailed study in English is: *The History of the British Film* in three volumes (London, 1948–50) by Rachel Low and Roger Manvell; I: 1896–1906; II: 1906–1914; III: 1914–1918. The most original work on international cinema history, and a real classic, is Terry Ramsaye's *A Million and One Nights* in two volumes (New York, 1926). Ramsaye knew most of the cinema pioneers personally. For this reason he overestimates Edison to the detriment of W. K. L. Dickson, as Gordon Hendricks has recently demonstrated in *The Edison Motion Picture Myth* (Berkeley and Los Angeles, 1961).

The following list includes some general works which deal briefly with cinema's early history only in the introduction or in the first chapter; most of the dates they give should be accepted with caution, for I have found considerable error here.

ALHAZEN (Ibn al Haitam): *Opticae Thesaurus Alhazeni Arabis*. Basel, 1572

ALLISTER, RAY: *Friese-Greene. Close up of an inventor*. London, 1948

BARDÈCHE, MAURICE and ROBERT BRASILLACH: *Histoire du Cinéma*. Engl. trans., New York, 1938

BLUM, DANIEL: *A pictorial History of the Silent Screen*. New York, 1953

BODE, WALTER: *Das Kleine Filmlexikon. Ein Taschenbuch über das gesamte Filmwesen*. Frankfurt and Vienna, 1954

BOSSERT, H. TH. and H. GUTTMANN: *Aus der Frühzeit der Photographie 1840–70, ein Bildbuch nach 200 Originalen*. Frankfurt a. M., 1930

BRUNEL, GEORGES: *La Photographie pour tous*. Paris, 1894

COOK, O. M.: *Movement in two Dimensions*. London, 1963

CROY, HOMER: *How Motion Pictures are made*. London, 1899

DAGUERRE, LOUIS JACQUES MANDÉ: *Historique et description des procédés du daguerréotype et du diorama*. Paris, 1839

DEMENY, GEORGES EMILE JOSEPH: *Les Origines du cinématographe*. Paris, 1909

DICKSON, W. K. L. and A. DICKSON: *History of the Kinetograph, Kinetoscope and Kinetophonograph*. London, 1895

DOST, WILHELM: *Vorläufer der Photographie. Beitrag zur allgemeinen Geschichte der Photographie*. Berlin, 1931

DOST, WILHELM and ERICH STENGER: *Die Daguerreotypie in Berlin 1839–1860*. Berlin, 1922

DU, Swiss monthly magazine, June 1952, special issue on Old Photography. Contains, among other articles: Arnold Kübler: 'Frühe Schweizerische Photos'; Erich Stenger: 'Als man anfing zu photographieren'; Erich Stenger: 'Hillotypie, die größte Schwindelunternehmung in der Geschichte der Photographie'; Tiphaigne de la Roche: 'Ein Prophet der Photographie'; Francis MacManus: 'Das Familienporträt'; 'Bekämpfer und Bewunderer der neuen Erfindung'; 'J. B. Isenrings Vorwort zum Katalog seiner Lichtbilderausstellung von 1840'; '*Ars Photographica*, ein lateinisches Lobgedicht auf die Photographie von Papst Leo XIII'.

DUCA, LO: *Hippolyte Bayard, der erste Lichtbildkünstler*. Paris, 1943

DUCA, LO: *Histoire du Cinéma*, Vol. 81 *Que sais-je?* Paris, 1947

EDER, JOSEF MARIA: 'Geschichte der Photographie'. In *Ausführliches Handbuch der Photographie*, vol. I/1. 4th ed. Halle, 1932

EICHSFELDER, BENJAMIN S.: *Filmgeschichte in Stichworten / Kleine Publizistische Beiträge*. Hagen, 1951

EISNER, L. H. and H. FRIEDRICH: *Das Fischer Lexikon. Film, Rundfunk, Fernsehen*. Frankfurt a. M., 1958

FESCOURT, HENRY (editor): *Le Cinéma des origines à nos jours*. Contains: G.-M. Coissac, 'Précisions sur l'histoire du cinématographe'. Paris, 1932

FORCH, CARL: *Der Kinematograph und das sich bewegende Bild. Geschichte und technische Entwicklung der Kinematographie bis zur Gegenwart*. Vienna and Leipzig, 1913

FOUQUE, VICTOR: *La Vérité sur l'invention de la photographie. Nicéphore Niepce, sa vie, ses essais, ses travaux*. Paris, 1867

FRANKLIN, JOE: *Classics of the Silent Screen. A Pictorial Treasury*. New York, 1959

FREUND, GISÈLE: *Histoire de la photographie en France*. Paris, 1935

FRIESE-GREENE, CLAUDE: 'How films began', Article in *The World Film Encyclopedia. A Universal Screen Guide*. Edited by Clarence Winchester, London, 1933

FÜLÖP-MILLER, RENÉ: *Die Phantasiemaschine. Eine Saga der Gewinnsucht*. Berlin–Vienna–Leipzig, 1931

GERNSHEIM, H. and A: *L. J. M. Daguerre. The History of the Diorama and the Daguerreotype*. London, 1956

GREGOR, JOSEPH: *Das Zeitalter des Films*. Vienna, 1932

GRIFFITH, RICHARD and A. MAYER: *The Movies. The sixty-year story of the world of Hollywood and its effect on America. From pre-Nickelodeon days to the present*. New York, 1957

GRIMOIN-SANSON, RAOUL: *Le Film de ma vie*. Paris, 1926

GUYOT, ABBÉ: *Nouvelles Recréations physiques et mathématiques*. Paris, 1770

HAAS, WILLY: 'Daguerre fixierte die Welt. Zum 100. Todestag des Erfinders der Photographie'. Article in *Die Welt*, July 11, 1951

HENDRICKS, GORDON: *The Edison Motion Picture Myth*. Berkeley and Los Angeles, 1961

HEPWORTH, CECIL M.: *The ABC of Cinematography*. London, 1897

HEPWORTH, CECIL M.: *Came the Dawn. Memories of a Film Pioneer*. London, 1951

HEYL, HENRY RENNO: 'A Contribution to the History of the Art of Photographing Living Subjects in Motion and Reproducing the Natural Movements by the Lantern', in *Journal*, The Franklin Institute CXV. Philadelphia, 1898

HOOPER, WILLIAM: *Rational Recreations*. London, 1774 and 1782

HOPWOOD, H. V.: *Living Pictures. Their History, Photo-Production and Practice Working*. London, 1899

HORAN, JAMES D.: *Mathew Brady. Historian with a Camera*. New York, 1955

JACOBS, LEWIS: *The Rise of the American Film. A critical history*. New York, 1939

JACKSON-WRIGLEY, M. and LANGLAND, ERIC: *The Cinema*. London, 1939

JEANNE, RENÉ and CHARLES FORD: *Histoire encyclopédique du cinéma* (I. Le Cinéma Français 1895–1929. Paris, 1947

KALBUS, OSKAR: *Vom Werden deutscher Filmkunst* (I. 'Der stumme Film'). Altona-Bahrenfeld, 1935

KIRCHER, ATHANASIUS: *Ars Magna Lucis et Umbrae*. Rome, 1646, Amsterdam, 1671

KIRCHER, ATHANASIUS: *Autobiography*. (German translation by N. Seng. 1901)

KLEINER, B. and M. LEUTENEGGER: *Film, dramaturgisch, gesellschaftlich, historisch*. Zürich, 1953

KOMROFF, MANUEL: *Mathew Brady*. Chicago, 1962

KUBNICK, HENRI: *Les frères Lumière*. Paris, 1936

LAPIERRE, MARCEL: *Les cent visages du Cinéma*. Paris, 1948

L'ESTRANGE, FAWCETT: *Die Welt des Films*. Freely adapted and supplemented for the German edition by C. Zell and S. Walter Fischer, with the collaboration of the German Cinema Association. Zürich, Leipzig and Vienna. n. d.

LIESEGANG, F. PAUL: *Marey, der Begründer der modernen Kinematographie*. Düsseldorf, 1910

LIESEGANG, F. PAUL: *Das lebende Lichtbild. Entwicklung, Wesen und Bedeutung der Kinematographie*. Düsseldorf, 1910

LIESEGANG, F. PAUL: *Lichtbild- und Kinotechnik*. München-Gladbeck, 1913

LIESEGANG, F. PAUL: 'Die Kinematographie vor 25 Jahren'. (Reprint from *Photographische Industrie.* 22, 1913)

LIESEGANG, F. PAUL: *Vom Geisterspiel zum Kino.* Düsseldorf, 1918

LIESEGANG, F. PAUL: 'Die Erfindungsgeschichte des Lebensrades'. (Reprint from *Die Kinotechnik.* 6, 1924)

LIESEGANG, F. PAUL: 'Der Stammbaum des Kinematographen'. (Reprint from *Kinotechnisches Jahrbuch* 1925/26)

LIESEGANG, F. PAUL: *Zahlen und Quellen zur Geschichte der Projektionskunst und Kinematographie.* Berlin, 1926

LIESEGANG, F. PAUL: 'Bemerkungen zu den Arbeiten von Ottomar Anschütz'. Supplement to the article in *Der Kinematograph,* 1908, No 100, Düsseldorf, 1936

LIESEGANG, F. PAUL (editor): *Die Projektionskunst und die Darstellung von Lichtbildern. Mit einer Anleitung zum Malen auf Glas und Beschreibung chemischer, magnetischer, optischer und elektrischer Experimente.* 12th edition, Leipzig, 1909

LONDE, ALBERT: *La Photographie moderne.* Paris, 1895

MAREY, ÉTIENNE JULES: *Le Mouvement.* Paris, 1894

MAYER, J. P.: *British Cinemas and their Archives.* London, 1948

MAYER and POIRSON: *La Photographie. Histoire de sa découverte.* Paris, 1862

MÉLIÈS, GEORGES: 'Les Vues cinématographiques'. (Article in *L'Annuaire général et international de la photographie.* 1907

MESSTER, OSKAR: *Mein Weg mit dem Film.* Berlin, 1936

MITRY, JEAN: *Index historique des techniques et industries du film.* Paris, 1963

MOHOLY, LUCIA: *A Hundred Years of Photography.* Harmondsworth, 1939

MORIN, EDGAR: *Le Cinéma ou l'homme imaginaire. Essai d'anthropologie sociologique.* Paris, 1956

MUSSCHENBROEK, PIETER VAN: *Physicae experimentalis.* Leyden, 1729, Venice, 1756

NEWHALL, BEAUMONT: *The History of Photography from 1839 to the Present Day.* New York, 1949

NOBLE, PETER (editor): *The British Film Yearbook,* contains 'Brief historical Survey of the British Film Industry', London, n. d.

NOVERRE, MAURICE: *Emile Reynaud, sa vie et ses travaux.* Brest, 1926

OERTEL, RUDOLF: *Filmspiegel. Ein Brevier aus der Welt des Films.* Vienna, 1941

OGDEN, C. K.: *Basic Motion Pictures.* Cambridge, 1937

PANOFSKY, WALTER: *Die Geburt des Films. Ein Stück Kulturgeschichte.* Würzburg, 2nd ed., 1944

PATHÉ, CHARLES: *Souvenirs et conseils d'un parvenu.* Paris, 1926

PORGES, FRIEDRICH: *Schatten erobern die Welt. Wie Film und Kino wurden.* Basel, 1946

PORTA, GIOVANNI BATTISTA DELLA: *Magia naturalis, sive de miraculis rerum naturalium.* Naples, 1558 and 1589

POTONNIÉE, GEORGES: *Histoire de la découverte de la photographie.* Paris, 1925

POTONNIÉE, GEORGES: *Les Origines du cinématographe.* Paris, 1928

QUIGLEY, JR, MARTIN: *Magic Shadows, The Story of the Origin of the Motion Pictures.* Washington D.C., 1948

QUIGLEY, JR, MARTIN: *Magic Shadows.* New York, 1960

RAMSEGER, GEORG: 'Zwei Erzväter der Photographie'. Article in *Die Welt*, April 4, 1963

RECHT, CAMILLE: *Die alte Photographie.* (Foreword by Iwan Goll). Paris and Leipzig, 1931

REINERT, CHARLES: *Kleines Filmlexikon. Kunst, Technik, Geschichte, Biographie, Schrifttum.* Einsiedeln-Zürich, 1946. (Little information on early history of cinema.)

ROBERT (ROBERTSON), ETIENNE GASPARD: *Mémoires récréatifs, scientifiques et anecdotiques du Physicien-Aéronaute.* Paris, 1831–33

ROTHA, PAUL: *The Film till Now.* London, 1949

ROTHA, PAUL and ROGER MANVELL: *Movie-Parade. 1888–1949, a Pictorial Survey of World Cinema.* London and New York, 1950

SADOUL, GEORGES: *Histoire de l'art du cinéma des origines à nos jours.* 3rd ed., Paris, 1949

SADOUL, GEORGES: *French Film.* London, 1953

SADOUL, GEORGES: 'Le centenaire d'Emile Reynaud', in *Les maîtres du cinéma, Cinématèque Française.* Paris, 1945

SENNETT, MACK (as told to Cameron Shipp): *King of Comedy.* New York, 1954

SPACIL, KARL: 'Franz Freiherr von Uchatius'. *Schweizerische Zeitschrift für Artillerie und Genie,* XLI. Frauenfeld, 1905

STENGER, ERICH: *Die beginnende Photographie im Spiegel von Tageszeitungen und Tagebüchern.* (Ein Beitrag zum hundertjährigen Bestehen der Lichtbildnerei 1839 bis 1939, nach hauptsächlich in der Schweiz durchgeführten Forschungen.) 2nd ed., Würzburg, 1943

STENGER, ERICH: *Siegeszug der Photographie in Kultur, Wissenschaft, Technik.* Seebruck, 1950

STILLMAN, D.: *The Horse in Motion.* London, 1882

TALBOT, FREDERICK A.: *Moving Pictures. How they are made and worked.* London, 1912

TAYLOR, DEEMS (with M. Peterson and B. Hale): *A Pictorial History of the Movies.* New York, 1943

THIEL, RUDOLF: *Ruhm und Leiden der Erfinder.* (Chapter on Uchatius: 'Tragödie eines Patrioten'). Berlin, 1942

THOMAS, DAVID B.: *The Origins of the Motion Picture.* London, 1964

THORNDIKE, LYNN: *History of Magic and Experimental Sciences.* New York, 1923–41

THUN, RUDOLF: *Entwicklung der Kinotechnik.* ('Abhandlungen und Berichte des Deutschen Museums', Heft 5). Berlin, 1936

TRAUB, HANS: *Als man anfing zu filmen.* Berlin, 1940

TRAUB, HANS and HANNS WILHELM LAVIES: *Eine Bibliographie der Bücher und Zeitschriften über das Filmwesen.* Leipzig, 1940

UCHATIUS, FRANZ: *Apparat zur Darstellung beweglicher Bilder an der Wand.* Sitzungsberichte der Akademie der Wissenschaften. Vienna, 1853

VIVIÉ, JEAN: *Traité général de technique du cinéma.* I: Historique et développement de la technique cinématographique. Paris, 1946

WACKERMANN, CARL: *George Eastman.* London, 1930

WATERHOUSE, JAMES: 'Notes on the early history of the Camera obscura', *Photographic Journal* XXV, 9. London, 1901

WEIMAR, WILHELM: *Die Daguerreotypie in Hamburg 1839–1860. Ein Beitrag zur Geschichte der Photographie.* I. Beiheft zum Jahrbuch der Hamburgischen Wissenschaftlichen Anstalten, XXXII, 1914. Hamburg, 1915

WOOD, LESLIE: *The Miracle of the Movies.* London, 1947

ACKNOWLEDGEMENTS

For permission to reproduce photographs in this book and for allowing objects in their collections to be photographed the author and the publisher are grateful to the following:

Mr Sidney Birt Acres · Mr Bernard Alfieri · The Barnes Museum of Cinematography, St Ives · M. Maurice Bessy · Bolwell Studios, Bath · The British Film Institute · The British Museum · Brown University, Providence · Mr J. Camponogara · The Cinématèque Française · The Cooper Union Museum, New York · George Eastman House, Rochester, New York · The Kingston-upon-Thames Corporation · Leeds Central Library · The Library of Congress, Washington · The Lytton Center of the Visual Arts, Hollywood · Musée Historique de Lyon · Museo del Cinema, Turin · Museum für Hamburgische Geschichte · Mr Percy Muir · The National Gallery, London · The National Portrait Gallery, London · The Newark Public Library, New Jersey · Oesterreichische filmwissenschaftliche Gesellschaft · The Royal Photographic Society · The Science Museum · The Scientific Instrument Company, Cambridge · Mr Edwin Smith · Mr George Speaight · Staatliche Landesbildstelle, Hamburg · The University Library, Cambridge · The Victoria and Albert Museum · Mr Friedrich von Zglinicki

Figures in italics refer to the illustrations